Guardians of Hidden Traditions

Cover Art
Rosa de Castilla
by Diana Bryer

This literary work brings much needed understanding and focus to the Jewish experience in Northern New Mexico. The historical and cultural contributions of New Mexico's Sephardic Jews is acknowledged and celebrated in this fine historical document. A gift of love for *su gente*.

-- David Rogers, Executive Director, Dual Language of New Mexico

This is a poignant account of history, family and self worth-- a true labor of love intertwining personal perceptions, rich heritage and tender blessings. Dr. Isabelle Sandoval's writing is skillfully elegant and sprinkled with heartfelt emotional truth.

-- Dr. Loretta Salazar, Professor, New Mexico Highlands University

Series

Western Sephardic Traditions

Isabelle Medina-Sandoval, Editor

Gaon Books about Western Sephardic life and history
from Europe to the Americas, exploring experiences from
the Diaspora, including crypto-Judaism.

Volume I
Cantos judeo-españoles:
simbología poética y visión del mundo
Silvia Hamui Sutton

Volume II
Guardians of Hidden Traditions,
Isabelle Medina-Sandoval

Volume III
Converso,
Mario X. Martinez

Isabelle Medina-Sandoval

Guardians of Hidden Traditions

Gaon Books
www.gaonbooks.com

Copyright © 2009

Manufactured in the United States of America

Library of Congress
Cataloguing-in-Publication Data:

Medina-Sandoval, Isabelle.
  Guardians of Hidden Traditions / Isabelle Medina-Sandoval. -- 1st ed.
      p. cm. -- (Series on Western Sephardic Traditions)
  Includes bibliographical references.
  ISBN 978-0-9820657-8-5
  1. Jews--Spain--Seville--History. 2. Jews--Persecutions--Spain--Seville--History. 3. Crypto-Jews--Spain--Seville--History. 4. Inquisition--Spain. 5. Spain--Ethnic relations--History. 6. Jews--New Mexico--History. 7. Crypto-Jews--New Mexico--History. 8. New Mexico--Ethnic relations--History. I. Title.

DS135.S75S448 2009
  305.892'404686--dc22

                          2009015632

British Cataloguing-in-Publication data for this book is available from the British Library.

Contents

Timeline....9
Introduction....11

Dedicated to my son, Tomás, and grandson, Jacob,
with deep appreciation of my mother and father
and my Sephardic *anusim* ancestors
guardians of our traditions

Timeline

1135 Maimonides born in Córdova, Spain
1200 Highly Developed Native Cultures in Southwest
1200 Kabbalah studied in Spain by Jewish Mystics
1391 Jews persecuted throughout Spain
1391 Solomón Halevi became Pablo de Santa María
1449 Limpieza de Sangre or "Purity of Christian Blood" established in Toledo
1479 Catholic Monarchs established Spanish Holy Office of the Inquisition
1492 Spanish Edict of Expulsion of Jews
1514 Edict of Grace established, becoming Edict of Faith
1519 Hernán Cortés landed in Mexico
1522 Mexican Inquisition started
1537 Pedro Robledo born in Carmena, Spain
1540 Coronado Expedition
1548 Catalina López born near Toledo, Spain
1557 Bartolomé Romero born in Corral de Almaguer, Spain
1590 Gaspar Castaño de Sosa Expedition in New Mexico
1596 Luis Carbajal burned at stake in Mexico City
1598 Juan de Oñate Expedition established San Gabriel
1605 *Don Quijote de la Mancha* published
1607 Jamestown established
1610 *Villa* of Santa Fe established
1620 *Comisario* Alonso Benavidez was agent of Inquisition in Santa Fe, NM
1620 Pilgrims established Plymouth Colony
1641 Catalina López Romero born in Santa Fe
1660 *Comisario* Alonso Posada was agent of Inquisition in Santa Fe, NM
1662 Six New Mexicans tried by Mexican Inquisition in Mexico City
1680 Pueblo Rebellion
1693 De Vargas Expedition, Velasco-Farfán Expedition to Santa Fe

1694	Páez Hurtado Expedition
1706	*Villa* of Albuquerque established
1716	*Comisario* Juan Tagle was agent of Inquisition in Santa Fe
1734	Miguel Quintana reported to Inquisition in Santa Fe
1755	María Paula Mascareñas born
1776	13 Colonies declared Independence from England
1810	Santuario de Chimayo built by Bernardo Abeyta
1820	Mexican Inquisition ended
1834	Spanish Inquisition ended

1391-1510

Spain

Sephardic History

Introduction

Various regional kingdoms prevailed over the Iberian Peninsula during the Middle Ages. Cities and villages from north to south and east to west were influenced by Iberians, Celts, Phoenicians, Greeks, Romans, Visigoths, Muslims, Jews and Christians. The two most influential provinces after the twelfth century were Castilla and Aragon. Isabel, Queen of Castilla, married Ferdinand, King of Aragon, in 1469, and this union joined the two large Spanish kingdoms into one.

Religious students of all faiths studied the *Mishneh Torah* written by Maimonides in Arabic. Famous Jewish writer and physician, Maimonides, was born in Córdoba and reared in medieval Muslim Spain. Later moving to Morocco, the center of Islamic religion, he learned quickly that practicing Jews were not tolerated. In his *Epistle on Martyrdom*, Maimonides stated that a persecuted Jew should publicly adopt Islam and maintain crypto-Judaism in private life. He died in 1204 in Egypt, away from his native Spain.

Kabbalah, meaning *that which is received,* arose as Jewish mysticism in twelfth century Spain. Mystical writing appeared in the Zohar in the thirteenth century. This thought embraced ten Sefirot, the process of G-d unfolding by spheres in the material world. The Sefirot appeared in a balanced tree representing the life and actions of G-d.

Christians, Jews, and Muslims lived in a community of tolerance and cooperation. This ambiance of *convivencia* was viewed as the ultimate harmonious state of cultural interdependence.

Jews usually lived in a certain area of a town. In the balance of creating respectful diversity by perpetuating Jewish culture, the *kahal*, Hebrew for the old Jewish quarter, had powerful walls to protect the Jews from the Gentiles. The houses had few windows and outside walls were white-washed. The central courtyards were decorated with flowers, vines and fruit trees. In the days before Christian dominance, Jewish homes were the gathering places for rabbis, physicians, Muslim scholars and Christian intellectuals. Poetry, science, mathematics, medicine, music, religion and philosophy were intellectual topics for discourse. Diversity was valued and persons of all backgrounds were treated with respect. Arabic, Spanish, Greek and Hebrew languages and cultures were exchanged freely within the discussion.

One important city in Spain was Toledo. The captivating city of Toledo. . .constructed on a hill and bordered by the Río Tajo on three sides of the city. On the fourth side, a fortified wall was built by Alfonso VI in 1085 as described in the epic poem of *El Cid Campeador*. Alfonso VI of Castilla took this region from the Moors and established the Christian *reconquista*. The spirit of *convivencia* encouraged religious diversity and by 1391, ten synagogues and five Talmudic schools served the Toledo Jewish population. Hebrew scholarship and spirituality in multilingual and multicultural perspectives were nurtured in this City of Generations.

Persecution of Jews throughout Spain for not practicing Christianity eventually impacted all Jewish communities. As a result of a decade of inflammatory statements made by Ferrán Martínez against Jews, on June 4, 1391, the Jews of Sevilla were attacked by Christian citizens. Martínez urged citizens to destroy the twenty-three synagogues, confine Jews to a ghetto and remove influential Jews from office. It is estimated that in 1392 Spain, 100,000 Jews converted; 100,000 Jews were murdered; and another 100,000 Jews fled the country. Meanwhile, as some Jews married into nobility, they were integrated into middle and upper socio-economic levels of Iberian society. The question of what it meant to be Jewish became more complex. Changing Christian Spain, inclusive now of Roman Catholic churches and accompanied by priests and religious lay persons, replaced Muslim caliphs and mosques from the Atlantic Ocean to the Mediterranean Sea. Some assimilated Jews saw their orthodox brothers and sisters as old-fashioned and behind modern times. Several orthodox Jews viewed the *conversos* as their competitors relative to financial and social advancement in society. At the same time, both of the sides recognized they were one people.

In 1449, the Toledo municipal authorities issued a pogrom targeting *conversos*. The documentation of *conversos* by the government alienated *conversos* from both the Christian and Jewish worlds. Suddenly, the spirit of *convivencia* ceased to exist and the *conversos* became the unwanted of Toledo society. Crypto-Jews lived in *sinvivencia* in a community brimming with intolerance and persecution. It was decreed that *conversos* were "unfit" to hold any office in Toledo or have any authority over Christians. The social structure in Toledo changed immediately because *conversos* were deemed as the lowest caste of any group in the city.

This statute, written in Toledo, became the precursor of the *limpieza de sangre* or the "purity of blood" mandate. Pope Nicholas V concluded that this ordinance was contrary to Catholic faith because *all* Catholics were one universal people. However, Spanish kings approved the racial laws in 1451. As church and society disapproved of Jews living in Spain, the argument that only Christians could live in Spain became apparent with each passing decade. The requirement of *limpieza de sangre* was instituted in 1555 in Spain and Portugal. As a result of this prerequisite, *conversos* created or falsified intricate genealogies to hide their Jewish ancestry. Spain, comparable in size to California, became a unified country in 1512 and was recognized as a world power.

Times were hard on crypto-Jewish families. Not only was Spain becoming more Catholic in spirituality and religion, citizens were obsessed with converting others to their faith and bringing religious uniformity to Castillian life. The *Santa Hermandad*, or Holy Citizen Police Force, had existed since the twelfth century to stop crime. Church bells would ring from community to community to warn citizens of criminal activity. *Los Reyes Catolicos*, Ferdinand and Isabel, later utilized this religious system in 1492 for mobilizing *La Hermandad* to provide for national law and order. The outcome of this union resulted in active citizen participation bridging Church and civil governance.

Spain, once the communal home of Jews, Arabs and Christians, was rallied by the intense spiritual cry of the *reconquista*. The new nation yielded to subjection by Catholic royalty. Finally, on March 31, 1492, *Don* Ferdinand and *Doña* Isabel, issued their Edict of Expulsion in Santa Fe, a town established between the Alhambra of Granada and the Alpujarra Mountains. This decree "commanded" all Jews, of all ages, to leave Spain by July 1492. The reason for the expulsion was due to "the great damage to Christians" by the Jews to "faithful Christians from our Holy Catholic faith."

The Alhambra Decree delineated Jewish practices designated by the Inquisitors. These "injurious" practices included: observance of the Law, reading and teaching of the Law, circumcision, prayer books, fasts, studying the history of the Law, observing Passover, and eating of certain foods correlating with the Law.

By the spring and summer of 1492, it is estimated that nearly 175,000 Jews left Spain. Another 100,000 chose to become *conversos* and unite with the augmenting number of their *converso* brothers and sisters yet living in Spain. For numerous reasons, almost half of the Jews in Spain would not or could not leave their country and accepted conversion.

How many Jews were tried by the Spanish Inquisition? It is believed that over 50,000 Jews were tried, convicted and executed in Spain during the first fifty years of the Inquisition. By 1514, the Edicts of Grace delineated Jewish customs for the Christian population. The purpose of the Edicts of Grace was to eradicate heresy from Spanish soil. However, the edicts also served as a guide for the *conversos* distanced from formal Hebrew teachings and synagogues. Christians were encouraged to report Jews to officials. The identity of Spanish citizens reporting Jews was kept secretive and not revealed to the accused. Jews were tortured, burned in effigy, burned alive and executed by other means. Those found guilty of being Jews had their assets confiscated by the authorities. If the accused guilty person had died, the body was exhumed and the bones were burned.

And this was a time in Iberian Spain commencing in 1391 that tarnished her forever as her Jewish native sons and daughters were banished from Spanish soil. It was nearly a century later in 1480 that King David's progeny heeded Maimonides' advice of professing Christianity and maintaining Judaism in the privacy of their homes. It was a dark period of *sinviviencia*. It was a time of not living together.

Part I
Spain, 1391 to 1572

June 4, 1391

Sevilla, Spain

Ferrán Martínez, Archdeacon of Éjica

Chapter 1

"Yes, we want to save their souls. If the Jews choose not to convert to the Holy Church, they must move to one designated area of the city. Only the Sacrament of Baptism will save them for eternal life. We all want and hope that Jews will become *cristianos lindos*," preached the olive skinned charismatic Spanish priest, Ferrán Martínez, with perceived celestial authority to the crowd gathering around him.

"It would be in the best interest of Sevilla if the synagogues were eradicated from our city. This way we will promote the righteousness of our Catholic faith." Pointing to the cross and bell adorning the Giralda, the tallest building in all of Sevilla, the masterful priest continued, "Look at the top of La Giralda. It was once a Muslim minaret serving as a call to prayer for the Muslims of Sevilla. The earthquake in 1365 toppled the copper sphere and it was replaced with the blessed cross of our Lord Jesus Christ. God will give us courage to fight this battle."

Extending his soft right hand in the direction of the Jewish quarter known as Santa Cruz, Martínez persisted, "Why do twenty-three synagogues serve as Jewish religious centers? We are Christians and we will not tolerate this heresy in our city. I am convinced that royalty would not harm or punish citizens destroying these so called religious centers."

Since 1378, the priest often spoke to small groups of citizens in towns surrounding Seville and Castile about his growing disdain for Jews. Speaking to the *pueblo menudo*, he sought to gain the trust and support of the common people. These same "little people" were supported actively behind the scenes by upper class individuals seeking their own lucrative ends.

As the mediocre priest, who had minimal formal education, examined the growing crowd of three hundred persons, he added, "Jews are incorrigible criminals. Their Muslim slaves can convert to Christianity and they will be freed. Look at their Jewish homes in Santa Cruz and see how well they live. Do you have the same luxuries?"

Vendors adjacent to the crowd and bordering the Alcázar, a tenth century palace built for the Moorish governors, appraised the growing crowd and gathered up their spices, textiles and *corda seca* pottery trimmed in gold and left. Innocent onlookers were afraid, and the negative energy of the crowd swept away everything before it like the tumultuous currents of the Guadalquivir River in springtime.

Ferrán Martínez was the archdeacon of Éjica and vicar general of the church in Seville. His average physical features were non-descript and his purpose in life was to rid Spain of the Jews. Serving as a judge, Martínez ruled that Jews could not live in Seville's archbishopric. Upset about the judge's ruling, Jews protested to King Enrique II. After the King died in 1379, the *Cortes* of Soria determined that Jews would no longer serve in noble positions and that Jews were barred from judging their own criminal cases.

Incited by the continual support from mounting essential sources, Martínez spoke to the *pueblo menudo* about the evil influence of the Jews on good Christian people. His inflammatory sermons acknowledged his hatred for Jews by advocating the destruction of synagogues and abolishing Jewish traditions.

Pursing his thin critical lips in fervent oratory, Ferrán Martínez heightened the seriousness of the moment with his persuasive conclusion to the large crowd stating, "Will you allow this heresy to grow in Sevilla? What would our Lord Jesus Christ say? The Jews are traitors, enemies of the faith."

By now, the crowd swelled to over a thousand angry persons. Heads bobbed up and down agreeing with Martínez as he spoke. No one voiced opposition to the abhorrent message preached by the Catholic priest.

One agitated middle-aged man, stocky and plump, was hoisted up in the air by his comrades and brothers. Anger and excitement crammed every nook and cranny of the growing angry crowd. The bald headed man, standing on the shoulders of his friends yelled, "Jews are criminals. They are the enemies of our sacred faith. Join me and let us tear down their synagogues and homes. Wait until I tell you the day and time that we will all reclaim our land for our faith."

With the impending quietness of the night hour darkening Sevilla for temporary slumber, the crowd dispersed. Then awakening with the ferocity of the power of the unfinished earthquake of 1365, on dawn of June 4, 1391, the *judería* of Santa Cruz was penetrated through its wooden gates by the *menudos*. Thousands of Jews were killed while thousands of Jewish women and children were sold into slavery.

The Jews spared of this bloody and psychological death were given the opportunity to be baptized. Over 20,000 Jews were truly frightened into requesting conversion and hurried to baptismal fonts. When the *conversos* returned to their homes, the homes had been ransacked, business and personal records were destroyed and the synagogues were ruined. Santa Cruz, home of the Jews of Sevilla, had virtually vanished.

The Jews of Sevilla were beyond demoralized. In the ashes of the once thriving *judería,* the Benaveda husband and wife, wept where their home once stood. What would they do? Everything they owned was gone. Where would they make their new home?

The Catholic Church or the Crown did not endorse the violence initiated by the priest eventually resulting in death and riot. However, the silence condoned the reprehensible actions promoted by Ferrán Martínez. Sevilla was finally rid of the Jews.

King Solomon wrote: *A season is set for everything, a time for every experience under heaven.* The toxic season in 1391 Iberian Spain tarnished herself forever as her Jewish native sons and daughters were victimized and murdered for being Jews.

July, 1391

Burgos, Spain

Conversion of Rabbi Solomón Halevi to Pablo de Santa María

Chapter 2

R eports about the Jewish annihilation in Sevilla spread quickly throughout the towns and cities. Innocent men, women and children were murdered because of their religious beliefs. To save their lives, many Jews in southern Spain were coerced into being baptized and becoming Christians. Jews referred to their brothers and sisters of this mandatory conversion of Spanish Jews as *anusim*, a Hebrew term meaning Jews forced to convert. A wave of shock and disappointment reverberated in Jewish households.

Soon after the rioting in Sevilla, the Jews of Córdoba were attacked. More than two thousand corpses were stacked along the synagogues, homes and streets. Many Cordoban Jews rushed to be baptized in order to escape death at the hands of the *menudos* and conniving *caballeros*. Citizens of all faiths felt the thick and growing cloud of mistrust, and Jewish communities all over Spain braced themselves for imminent attacks.

Directly north of Madrid, panic engulfed the Jewish population of Burgos. Jews populated this city in the eleventh century. Burgos was considered one of the leading political centers of Castile. The Cathedral of Burgos, constructed in 1222, mirrored French Gothic influence. Fancy filigree spires adorned the lavish spiritual edifice.

Christian pilgrims stopped in the city to and from their journey to the shrine of Santiago de Compostela. The sacred site was revered because it was believed that the bones of

Saint James were buried here. Santiago de Compostela was the place where a shepherd saw the star leading to the shrine of Saint James.

On June 16, 1391, government officials notified Jews in Burgos about the danger of possible riots. The anti-Jewish movement was moving to the north and danger was imminent.

One notable Jewish citizen of Burgos was Solomón Halevi. Raised in a rich Jewish family originally from Aragon, Halevi was proficient in Jewish law and literature. Halevi was well versed in Latin and studied the religious works of Thomas Aquinas. Because of his profound worldy religious knowledge, Halevi was appointed as Chief Rabbi of Burgos. Halevi was the leader of the Jewish constituency and fostered strong political as well as social ties in Castile. Having an affinity for high society and social amenities, it is said that he kept a carriage and footmen for his personal use to emulate prestigious government officials.

During Purim of 1389, a Jewish holiday of festivity celebrating the victory of Jews over the Persian oppressor Hamman by Queen Esther, Halevi wrote a jovial Purim letter to Rab *Don* Meir Alguadex. While he was on a vacation in France, Halevi communicated that he was not living in the encampment of the *Shekinah*. Joking about his separation from the feminine Kabbalah gate to another rabbi, his words may have illuminated the pathway for *conversos* who later regarded Saint Esther as a triumphant figure of crypto-Jewish accomplishment. These words written by Rabbi Halevi may have been an unconscious dark harbinger of the rabbi's personal spiritual future.

On July 21, 1391, the same Salomón Halevi, Chief Rabbi of Burgos, converted to the Catholic faith along with his five young children, mother, brother and sister. His new name was Pablo de Santa María. His Jewish wife, Juana, was baptized almost forty years later in 1430, close to her death.

On August 12, 1391, riots broke out in Burgos against the Jews. More Jews were murdered. Threatened by the atrocities committed in Sevilla and Córdova, Burgos Jews were somewhat more prepared to accept Christian baptism to save their lives. An entire quarter of *conversos* grew immediately in the city after August 12. Perhaps the abrupt conversion of Rabbi Halevi shaped the willingness of Jews to accept baptism rather than death from the atrocities of the *menudos.*

It was the summer of 1391 when the Romero family from Toledo rested by the juniper and oak trees in Burgos on their pilgrimage to Santiago de Compostela to visit the shrine of Saint James. Although they were *conversos* from nearby La Mancha, the recent pogroms frightened the family into displaying an outward appearance of being devout Catholics. As the family gazed on the magnificence of the architectural structures of the Cathedral of Burgos, the Romero family discussed the Jewish importance of visiting the bones of their ancestors.

Vicente Ferrer, Dominican friar of probable Jewish descent, was credited with being the key spiritual advisor to Pablo de Santa María by winning his soul over to the one true church. Adamant about bringing Jews into Christianity, the friar toured cities of Castile preaching to many persons. He claimed he did not want compulsory conversion yet forced Jews in the *juderías* to attend his sermons. As he walked from city to city, hundreds of flagellants, whipping themselves with chains, accompanied him. These zealots, singing somber hymns, reverently scourged themselves as they walked along with their leader. Ferrer was viewed by his followers as the pinnacle of devout Dominican penitential dedication. Observers were threatened and frightened by the large crowds and display of blood masked in the oratory of the piety of the friar.

Ferrer advocated that Jews should live apart from Christians and *conversos*. In 1412, in Valladolid, Jews were forced to give up their homes in order that they would be separated from social and religious interactions with Christians. Filthy and unsanitary residences were assigned to Jews. Now Jews were ordered to dress modestly as well as being excluded from working for the government and the court. These actions marked the future framework for the Inquisition regarding *conversos*.

Vicente Ferrer and Pablo de Santa María jointly influenced each other. Ferrer was the revered Catholic practitioner modeling penitence while preaching for uniformity of Christianity without the adverse influence of Jews. Catholics were intrigued with the complete conversion of Pablo de Santa María. The former rabbi became one of the supreme anti-Jewish leaders in Spain. Catholic historians wrote that the edict of 1412 was the result of Pablo's influence to bring about the destruction of Judaism and the escalation of the Catholic faith.

Later, other *conversos* recanted their Jewish faith and became clergymen. Following the footsteps of Pablo de Santa María, some of these men, personally knowing the Jewish faith, persecuted and intimidated their own fellow Jews or simply took vows to hide behind the protection of the Catholic Church.

It was highly probable that Pablo de Santa María converted because of the extremity of Jewish discrimination in Spain. He was forty years old at conversion and truly entered into adult wilderness until his death. Pablo, once the Chief Rabbi of Burgos, became the Bishop of Cartagena. Rabbi Halevi's conversion was a terrible shock for Spanish Jewry, and he was accused of contributing to the victimization of the Iberian *anusim*.

Ultimately, the Halevi family married into many prominent families. As this *converso* family multiplied, King Felipe III issued a royal decree recognizing the papal brief written by Pope Clement VIII in 1596. This papal dispensation was issued in the spirit of affirming the "*limpieza de sangre*" to the descendants of the Halevi family. The purpose of the special consideration of this Halevi family was because Pope Clement VIII believed family members descended from the same Hebrew tribe as the Virgin Mary. This dispensation legitimized the Catholic Halevi *limpieza de sangre*.

Pablo de Santa María did not have to falsify his Jewish genealogy to hide the pureness of his blood. The dispensation issued by Pope Clement VIII proved beyond a doubt that the Halevi family was not Levite but descended from the tribe of the Virgin Mary.

It was a time in Spain when crosses shadowed and obliterated mezuzahs during the shared Iberian sunrise and sunset. It was a time for weeping.

1449

Toledo, Spain

Doña Robledo

Chapter 3

The fifty-five year old woman walked cautiously to the small bedroom in the back of the house situated in the *judería* of Toledo. *Doña* Robledo stroked the altar cloth her grandmother made for the synagogue. It was a cream colored silk cloth embroidered with fine silk strands from Granada depicting the Tree of Life. Her grandmother told her the Tree of Life symbolized the Ten Commandments. Although outsiders often commented on the obvious conclusion that the tree was representative of the Garden of Eden, few individuals grasped the hidden significance of the teaching of the Law. Her grandmother always adorned the embroidery with pomegranates because the fruit represented fertility and life.

Doña Robledo gently touched the golden brown eagle with extended wings on the fine silk cloth. Her grandmother said the phoenix and eagle of Toledo were the same bird because it never died. After living a thousand years and being consumed by fire, the eagle rose from the ashes to live another thousand years. She often said that despite many trials, the eagles, like the Jewish people, would survive. Lamenting the pogroms across Spain forcing Jews to become *conversos,* the grandmother said that Jews and *conversos* were one people.

On this Shabbat, *Doña* Robledo lit the olive oil clay candleholders with the raised menorah ceramic motif. Closing her eyes and moving her hands to inhale the holy smoke, she prayed:

"Bendito seas Tú, Eterno, Dios nuestro, rey del universo que nos santificaste con tus mandamientos y nos ordenaste prender las velas de la fiesta."[a]

Doña Robledo prayed silently that *El Eterno* would always protect her children and grandchildren. She prayed that even though her family had been baptized under duress, she asked that G-d would remember how she washed off the Catholic baptism of all her children and grandchildren. The priests told the Jews that only Catholic baptism would save their souls. *Doña* Robledo always washed off the Catholic baptism because this religion did not believe in one G-d. The Ten Commandments did not include a Jesus Christ or a Virgin Mary. The statues of a melancholy mother and a suffering bloody son in the churches frightened her. She had to de-baptize her children because her own identity was shaped by the traditions of her mothers living the language of Jewish rituals. Her own mother sponsored the medieval Sephardic custom of the *hadas'* celebration for newborn babies. *Hadas* were the fairies bringing good luck and prosperity for the recent born baby.

In June 1391, eight synagogues in Toledo were destroyed. Jews were murdered and mass baptisms took place. Few Jews returned to the appointed *judería* and sought safe residences in outlying areas of the city. At this moment in 1449, citizens of Toledo accused the Jews of requiring the *menudos* to pay higher taxes. Several *conversos* were condemned to death by fire.

On January 27, 1449, murder, robbery and confiscation of property took place in the *judería* of Toledo. As the voices of the angry *menores* were heard in the streets as they ravaged the *judería*, *Doña* Robledo rushed to the Cathedral of Toledo to be baptized. Her altar cloth was burned in the looting. Nothing of the home was left. The aging old woman left to find a home with friends and family outside of the city once regarded as the prized jewel of Sephardic Judaism.

Effective 1449, Jews in Toledo could not hold any public office or have any authority over any Christians or the Holy Catholic Church. It was a time of perilous persecution of people believing in *El Eterno*.

The Inquisition became more active in Toledo to signify the "Act of Faith" sentiment. On February 12, 1486, 750 women and men from seven parishes filed in a procession through the streets sentenced to numerous penances. Over 900 penitents from six parishes were punished on April 2, 1486. Another 750 men and women Jewish penitents repeated the same procession on June 11, 1486. It was estimated that that there were 2,400 penitents in the year 1486. By May, 1487, twenty-three Jewish persons were executed.

Archival material was not gathered to record this massive conversion and abuse. And above the *judería*, the golden eagle of Toledo was consumed in the fire of the martyred Jews. It was a time for weeping.

1520

La Mancha, Spain

Maternal Kabbalistic Blessing

Chapter 4

*E*l *ingenioso hidalgo Don Quijote de la Mancha,* the classic novel of Spain by Miguel de Cervantes, was published in 1605. In writing Europe's first novel Cervantes satirized the chivalric traditions of the knight refusing to face the facts of ig-nobility in Catholic Spain. Meanwhile, crypto-Jews were confronted by the challenge of chasing hidden Jewish windmills in La Mancha. These religious hostages were living the impossible dream in a Spain where Judaism was outlawed the by the government and the church.

At the point in time of *Don Quijote,* in the real land of La Mancha, the López, Benadeva, Robledo and Romero surnames were known in the underground Jewish communities of Castilla as "New Christian" or *converso* surnames. Some family members were loyal secret Jews posing as Catholics in Christian Spain. These *converso* persons of Jewish extraction were representative of numerous families practicing a new synthesis of clandestine Judaism while pretending to be observant Catholics.

Women remembered the *cuentos* of their grandmothers reliving the nights of vigorous discourse analyzing the oral tradition of the Kabbalah and describing spiritual revelations. Long, energetic conversations by family members and honored guests after a Shabbat meal focused on the *Sha'are Orah* of Joseph Gikatilla. Born in 1248 in Castilla, Rabbi Joseph stressed the goodness of all creatures. Spanish Jews openly discussed the role of Kabbalah within Judaism. As the Inquisition shadowed

Jewish spiritual hopes in Spain, the oral tradition in the inner crypto-Jewish circle of the Kabbalah illuminated the knowledge of G-d in the creation.

Wrinkled facial lines etched by the worries of the oldest woman mapped the trials of her life. A granddaughter of prestigious Jewish ancestry, her family moved from the *judería* of Toledo to the countryside of Toledo to distance themselves from the immediate scrutiny of ecclesiastical authorities. Her grandfather was a wool merchant. Like other *conversos*, he was baptized under duress in Toledo to be a new convert in the Catholic Church, along with many other crypto-Jews from his old synagogue.

Succumbing to the societal, economic and religious pressure exerted on his family, he became a member of the *Cofradía de Santa María la Blanca* by 1478. The *cofradía* was primarily a powerful male Catholic religious society modeling Christian precepts. This society was akin to the Jewish confraternities regulating learning, charity, order and burial practices. Like other Catholic confraternities, the *cofradía* members wore a black tunic with a black hood during *Semana Santa* or Holy Week prior to Easter. This clothing mirrored the apparel worn by Inquisition dignitaries.

The grandfather would tell his granddaughter, with tears brimming from his eyes, of the day in 1454 when *San* Vicente Ferrer took *Santa María la Blanca Sinagoga* away from the Jews. *San* Vicente despised the Jews and was responsible for agitating the pogrom in Sevilla. A fiery Catholic leader, he was recognized for starting *La Cofradía de Santa Vera Cruz* in nearby Palencia. Later, the *cofradía* of Palencia became part of the *Hermandad* in 1575.

The family had worshipped in this beautiful Arabic mosque-style synagogue. The *abuelito* wept when he told his granddaughter of his hope of his family returning to Judaism in *Santa María la Blanca*, to pray the way his family had always worshipped. Constructed in 1203 by Joseph ben Shushan, the majestic horseshoe arches of this edifice were embellished with intricate pinecone decorations. This beloved synagogue, within the walls of the city of Toledo, was situated close to the Synagogue of the *Tránsito*.

The grandfather privately acknowledged his Jewish ancestry and only wished that his family could have escaped to a safe place. Although the family tried to relocate, it was made difficult by the factions trying to harm secret Jews. He told his granddaughter how he maintained close ties with other New Christians who were the merchants of Toledo. Putting his silver-haired head down on the oak table, he sobbed as he told her how a close male relative was processed by the Inquisition and how his *sambenito* was hung from the wall of *la Catedral de Toledo* for Judaizing.

This elegant aging woman, dressed in a frayed black silk gown with embroidered birds reminiscent of Muslim Spain, was honored in her family. She always observed the beginning of Shabbat in the back room of the lowly rural *casa*. She washed her hands slowly as she meditated on the meaning of Friday evening. She placed the black floral silk lace *mantilla* on her head and walked to the doorway of the bedroom. Touching the doorway in the invisible area of her imaginary mezuzah, she prayed that the *Eterno* would help her remember the Law. With her words and her prayers, she transmitted maternal secrets from one generation to another.

The white haired old woman spoke of how her father would meditate to ascend the order of the Sefirot as taught by Rabbi Gikatilla. As a young girl, the elderly woman was encouraged to listen to the religious discussions. As the strengthening anti-Jewish Spanish society forced this old woman into her hiding Jewish practices, the maternal leader changed her prayer to have her children survive this Iberian desolation. The *viejita* remembered to seek Adonay in the lower Sefirot and then progressed to higher levels in prayer by petitioning for her children to the highest holy gate. Each Shabbat she prayed for the survival of her children and unborn descendants. Like Hannah, this wise woman prayed in earnest simplicity. Hannah's mental prayer with her Maker was a close sharing of dialog between friends.

Daughters of the matriarch spoke of the grandmother sitting under her favorite olive tree situated near the home. The *viejita* compared the olive tree to the Tree of Life of the *Gates of Light* and extolled the beauty of the *Zohar*, the Book of Splendor.

Under the green umbrella of the olive tree, the grandmother meditated and reflected on her blessings. She prayed out loud in a whispering steady voice, "*Lámpara es para mi pie tu palabra, y luz para mi senda.*"[b]

This grandmother could not leave Spain in 1492 because she had no money and no one to help her travel. She followed the advice of Maimonides to practice Judaism privately and to observe Catholicism in public. Her grandfather told her that he remembered hearing about a *conversa* in Ciudad Real praying that even the dreams of her children in captivity would belong to Adonay. As each passing year grew harsher, this grandmother prayed that all the dreams of all of her future offspring would belong to the Eternal One.

A lonely tear trickled down the wrinkled cheek of the aging woman. The *abuelita* recalled walking the streets of Toledo of her home to the *sinagoga* now made into a Catholic church. How could holy words be a lamp on her path when she had to hide being a Jewess? At that moment, the *abuelita* realized that the oral tradition of the Kabbalah and the teaching of Rabbi Joseph Gikatilla provided a holy lamp of words to light her path. It was a time for the blinding invisible white light of the highest gate of the Kabbalah to save her progeny.

1572

Toledo, Spain

Catalina López de Robledo

First Generation

Chapter 5

Awakening from a rejuvenating sleep, Catalina blinked her eyes as she realized that it was Monday morning. Her mother's sister, *Tía* Ana, had prepared a fresh brew of Moroccan mint tea in the ceramic blue and white teapot she purchased recently at the market. It was the newest design from China the vendor in the Zocodover was selling.

"*Tía, gracias, gracias,*" whispered Catalina. "It has been such a long time since anyone has made breakfast for me. You know this is probably my last visit to see you before we find out if we are accepted to journey to Mexico and leave Spain. I will miss you very much."

"*Ay,* my precious niece, I will miss you more than you will ever know. You need to be pampered. Living outside the city of Toledo where you live in the small *pueblo* of Carmena must be difficult for you. You were raised in the lovely city of our people and we are accustomed to the luxuries the vendors sell as well as the activity of a city," answered the aunt.

Stroking the sugar white skin of her aunt's face, Catalina reached over and kissed *Tía* Ana on the cheek. Ana's black and silver hair, twisted in a bun, framed her fine features and accentuated her slender body. Dressed in a light wool dark brown dress, *Tía* Ana was a widowed middle-aged woman engaging in sewing to earn a living.

Gazing at the ceramic blue and white floral planter wedged against the ledge of the black grilled balcony, Catalina's thoughts drifted to her oldest daughter, Ana. Her daughter was a sickly child with acute breathing problems. Only nine years old, Ana was a frequent patient of the doctor. A beautiful auburn haired girl, Ana was often fatigued from mere daily exertion.

Sensing that Catalina was worrying about something, *Tía* Ana said, "You have been like my own daughter, Catalina. Since the day your mother, my sister, died from a tragic fall when you were five-years old, you became the daughter I never had. Speaking frankly, my dear niece, I have to share with you that I am concerned about the motives your Pedro may have. Please be careful around your husband because he may be reporting on you to the Inquisition. It often happens that family members and spouses turn on their loved ones," exclaimed Ana.

Catalina's countenance fell and she said, "Yes, I do understand. Even though Pedro comes from a *converso* family, I am not sure about his loyalty to me or to our faith. I will have to be careful just in case he does betray me."

"Try not to worry. Time will reveal the evidence of his true heart. Enjoy these few days with me. Just look at you now. You are almost thirty years old and you look just like my mother. *Barukh Hashem.* Your long black, curly long hair and green eyes melt the hearts of women and men. Your infectious laughter draws everyone to you. Come, sit at the table and eat," commanded *Tía* Ana.

The table was covered with *bretaña*, a superior British linen tablecloth. Snow white ceramic dishes from nearby Talavera painted with finely decorated indigo blue and yellow flowers were placed on the table. Bowls of almonds, dried figs, olives with herbs, pungent oranges, fresh white cheese and *mazapán* graced the white tablecloth.

Lifting the large linen napkin to uncover a fresh plate of *buñuelos*, *Tía* Ana told Catalina, "I fried these just for you, my sweet. My neighbor, *Doña* Esperanza, gave me some fresh pressed olive oil to fry the *buñuelos.*"

"Oh, *Tía*, they are just like the ones Mother said her grandmother made in the *judería* of Tudela," exclaimed Catalina as her two small hands broke a large fried bread with a hole in the center of the soft amber circle.

Layering the top of the golden puffy bread with a thick coating of honey, she said, "Mmm, I have not tasted such delicacies since I was a young girl."

Standing up from her chair to perform a forgotten task, *Tía* Ana returned quickly with a small Talavera white and blue vase filled with delicate small yellow roses.

"I went to the *judería* of my father near the old synagogue of *Santa María de la Blanca* to pick these flowers for you, my precious darling. This flower is called the *rosa de castilla* and the Arabs brought it centuries ago to grow in the *patios* of Spain when all people in Toledo lived peacefully with one another," said *Tía* Ana.

"*Gracias, Tía* Ana, the flowers are more than lovely. *Tía* Ana, our little Ana is sick. No one knows why she tires so easily. The doctor tells me to make her tea of *alhucema* to help her rest. I do not know if the lavender is helping her. In fact, Ana suggested she stay behind with her uncle, *Tío* Alejo, in Carmena. Luis, Pedro's nephew, promised me he would entertain her when he was not working in the vineyards," confided Catalina to her aunt.

Ana studied Catalina's troubled face and said, "Do not worry, *mi hija*. It will all work out."

With a big sigh of relief, Catalina replied, "How can I ever thank you properly, my aunt?" The women drank tea and ate heartily. Meanwhile, Catalina's seven-year-old daughter, Luisa, joined mother and great-aunt for a late breakfast and she had a voracious appetite for honey and almonds.

A small cry pierced the air, and Catalina bent down to lift her small baby. "My *hijo*, my son," and she hugged her six-month old Diego as she patted his back with tender motherly love.

"*Tía* Ana, will you watch Diego for me this morning while Luisa and I go to the market to buy some items I need?" asked Catalina.

"Go, go. I am happy to watch my little Diego. He is a good baby," replied the aunt as she caressed Diego in her arms.

Catalina changed into her navy blue wool dress and matching wool *mantón*, which she used as a shawl. By trade, Catalina was a weaver and her passion was visiting the market to view the quality clothing and ceramic merchandise. Her wool dress would shield her from the cool wind chilling Toledo.

Dressing Luisa in a matching dress and *mantón*, the mother and her seven-year old daughter walked through the old Bisagra Gate, underneath the double-headed eagle. They walked past homes and eventually arrived at the clamorous market of Zocodover. Rich odors of expensive saffron and abundant varieties of Chinese tea permeated the air.

She haggled over prices as she purchased spices, silk cloth from Granada and even splurged on buying a ceramic teapot from China. Falling in love with the fat belly of the pudgy white and blue floral abstract patterned teapot, Catalina thought the design was utilitarian and yet stylish. By packing the teapot in wool to cushion it on the trip to Mexico, the sturdy pot could be enjoyed later in a new country.

While meandering through the market place, one merchant's wares caught Catalina's eye. The vendor had hundreds of damascene products made of exquisite Toledo steel and etched with silver, copper and gold. Her eyes fixed on a small brooch with two intertwined triangles. The pin with the star of David captivated her and the merchant asked if she wanted to see the pin.

Realizing immediately that her affinity for Jewish symbols constituted danger for her loved ones, made her think about the outcome of her actions. This selfish attitude could jeopardize the safety of her family and she told the vendor that she was a solid Old Christian woman studying the craftsmanship of a Muslim design. Her head raced with logical reasons to substantiate her excuse.

Haltingly, the merchant put the pin back and told Catalina that although the design was Arabic, Jews were known to favor it as a symbol of good fortune. He said that Jews claimed it represented the greatness of King David.

Catalina stammered, "I-I-I am but a poor Old Christian woman. I really need to buy a cross to protect me from all hindrances and cannot afford such a luxury. I am not interested in an infidel Jewish amulet."

As she turned her back to leave the booth, a man with piercing *piñon*-colored eyes established direct eye contact with her. His perceptive look burned to the center of her heart. He looked through Catalina with abject disgust while shaking his head and muttering inaudible comments.

An ice-cold blast gripped her being. She and Pedro were trying to gain permission to go to Mexico City to live with Pedro's cousins. Such reckless behavior on her part might stain their future forever. A nervous twitch of her eye distorted her vision.

Holding Luisa's hand tightly to comfort herself, Catalina stopped at the candy booth and bought her daughter some creamy *turrón*. The rich nougat, flavored with rose water and toasted almonds, melted in Luisa's mouth, who begged for more and more to satisfy her unending sweet tooth. Not even the assurance that her mother had purchased an extra bag of candy quenched the fire of her inquiring hazel eyes, absorbing the recent spiritual confrontation.

Leaving the noisy market, Catalina breathed a deep sigh of relief. She relaxed as she found her way back to her aunt's home and reflected on the words of her father. Catalina's father died of a broken heart grieving her mother's death. Catalina remembered her father's gentle voice telling her that the Romans arrived in Toledo 192 years after the birth of the Rabbi Jesus. He confided in her that the devoutly Jewish López family was living in Toledo when the Romans arrived. His rabbi told him that the city was named *Toldoth* for generations of the Ten Tribes of Israel living there. She felt comforted knowing that thirteen centuries of her family had lived in Toledo. It was the cradle of generations of the family.

Nearing the synagogue her father had lovingly told her his great-grandfather attended, Catalina gave Luisa another candy and walked to the former synagogue her father had taken her to when she was smaller than her own Luisa. As mother and daughter approached the distinctive large building, emotions of apprehension and abandonment overwhelmed Catalina. A warm feeling overcame her anxiety as she sensed her father's comforting presence.

Catalina López de Robledo, native of Toledo, wife of Pedro Robledo and mother of Ana, Luisa, Luis and Diego, stood in front of the *Santa María la Blanca Iglesia.* Her father explained regretfully that the synagogue had no women's gallery and that he believed women needed to study Judaism. In 1550, Cardinal Martínez Siliceo converted the building into a house of charity for new penitents. She remembered her father telling her about his family worshipping in this synagogue. Now, the synagogue was Catholic property and had been denuded of Jewish artifacts.

Squeezing Luisa's tired hand, Catalina caught her breath as her emerald eyes sparkled with the spiritual richness of her father's family. She felt a hand tug on her arm and thought Luisa wanted her to pick her up and carry her for the remainder of the journey to her aunt's home.

Slicing the cool air with stormy velocity, a deep voice echoed, "You are the same *señora* I saw shopping in the Zocodover earlier this afternoon. I observed you admiring the Jewish brooch on display at the market. It is extremely odd that you like Jewish symbols," spouted the man in a condemning tone.

Cautiously, Catalina peered into the man's *piñon*-colored brown eyes and said, "I had never seen that pattern. I am but a poor weaver and was taken by the splendor of the metal artistry. I am unable to afford to buy such unneeded purchases when my daughter needs new clothing. I am a good Catholic woman," responded Catalina.

"And I am Padre Martínez, the priest, visiting this house of charity for earnest penitents. I would venture to say that your grandparents were New Christians. Is there a confession you would like to make to me?" he inquired while his hot eyes seared through her soul.

"Yes, Padre Martínez, I ask that you pray that a poor mother like me will find the resources to buy cloth to make her daughter a new dress," she replied in a soft whisper.

Moving his face within inches of her, he answered, "I will pray for you and I will keep you in my prayers. My job is to burn out heresy in the Church of the Lord Jesus Christ. *Cristo* is the Son of God. May Spain never forget that we live because we worship the Trinity," he retorted with mocking sarcasm. Lifting the heavy silver cross hanging on his chest, the priest kissed the crucifix and walked inside the building to pray for her soul. He looked back at her and made the sign of the cross as if he were casting out devils from this modest woman standing before him.

Calmly, Catalina crossed her heart and walked away from the danger of the old synagogue of her father's family. She stood a block away from the old *Santa María de la Blanca* edifice and whispered to Luisa, "Look at this building and burn its image in your memory. This is the place of worship of your mother and her family," said Catalina.

"Yes, *Mamacita*, I will always remember it forever," replied Luisa looking up at the structure as her curly hair cascaded in perfect ringlets. A fine white film like sweet Sabbath candles engulfed the entrance doors of the former synagogue.

Breathing a sigh of relief, Catalina reached down and drew her daughter close to her heart. She kissed her on the cheek and put her back down on the ground.

Above the resounding street noises of horses' hooves and heavy wooden carts, a cultured voice broke through the air. As Catalina was standing up, the refined voice quieted another impending storm. A quick fright overcame Catalina's body as she turned in the direction of the voice.

"What a lovely young daughter you have, my dear," crooned a smiling woman dressed in a rich burgundy silk Spanish farthingale hoopskirt. The stranger reached over and patted Luisa's perfect curls.

"My name is Catalina López de Robledo and this is my daughter, Luisa," answered Catalina cautiously.

"And I am María Adeva de Romero, from the town of Corral de Almaguer. I came to shop in Toledo and visit this old 'church' of my mother's ancestors. My father changed our name from Benadeva to Adeva when the expulsion was mandated by His Catholic Majesty.ᶜ I have missed the commotion of the city because I reside in such a small town. I am visiting the market and viewing the latest fabrics and dress styles. It is one of the few pleasures that I have in my old age."

Catalina looked intently into María's light brown eyes. Her eyes were shaded by the black lace *mantilla* covering her chestnut hair.

"I know, I understand. You are afraid. When I first saw you earlier at the market admiring the jewelry, I decided to purchase something for your daughter. Here you lovely little girl, I have a gift for you," said *Doña* María, smiling, as she gave Luisa a blue silk hanky.

"*Gracias, mil gracias*," responded Luisa as she unknotted the expensive hanky. Inside the handkerchief Luisa found the rich damascene pin her mother coveted earlier in the day.

"Luisa will treasure the pin always," said Catalina as she knotted the silk cloth and placed it in her parcels. The soft Granada silk fabric would also serve as a remembrance of a stranger's kindness in a dangerous city.

The three generations of women standing several hundred feet away from the synagogue of their families embraced each other. The feminine figures had their heads covered with textile scarves. Burning a hole through the thick gray clouds, the sun suddenly beamed rays of light on them. The *Shekinah* radiated on her righteous, vulnerable and exiled women of a changing Toledo.

Then they parted, never to see each other again in this world. As they separated, the sun retreated behind the dark clouds as if to cry. It was a time for war. It was a time for anxiety. Like the life of 1572 Toledo, it was covered by somber clouds. Toledo was even darker than the 1597 painting of the "View of Toledo" by the artist, Domenikos Theotokopoulos, known as El Greco. As dusk turned to evening, the old synagogue was but a forgotten memory in Catholic Spain. Both Catalina and *Doña María* were suspended in the living purgatory of practicing Catholicism while remembering Jewish parents.

1572

Carmena, Spain

Catalina López de Robledo

First Generation

Chapter 6

Returning home to Carmena on Thursday, Catalina woke up Friday morning eager to prepare for *sábado.* Her first thoughts were about her painful good-bye with *Tía* Ana with whom she had a special bond. Her *Tía* was the only mother she had really known. Even though Carmena was only twenty-five miles away from Toledo in eastern La Mancha, Catalina sensed a whole new world separating her from her aunt.

Closing her eyes in bed, she reflected on the move across an unknown ocean to a foreign land. It was exciting and also frightening to contemplate leaving her birthplace forever. Reaching over to kiss Pedro, she found only a pillow because Pedro left home earlier in early morning for business. Pedro was always confiding in someone about hushed matters.

It was the beginning of the new day. Her grandmother taught her to start the day by saying, *"Modah Ani,"* to thank G-d for returning her soul to her in the morning.

Climbing out of bed, she washed her hands and combed her hair. Finding the broom to remove the dust, she swept the dirt from the corners of the room to the center of the floor. Gathering the dirt in a container, she walked ten paces away from the house and threw the debris to the winds. She dusted household items in the house and found the new olive oil for making the Shabbat candles. Luisa helped watch Diego, Ana and Luis as her mother cleaned the house.

In the afternoon, Catalina started to make a Sabbath dish with a few new additions of herbs. The mental recipe she followed was given to her during the recent visit to Toledo. *Tía* Ana's best friend, Luz, told her how Beatriz García, who was tried by the Inquisition in 1528, had made Sabbath stew. First Catalina pounded fresh garlic with the mortar and pestle. With the recently purchased herbs of onion, dried coriander, caraway, cumin and pepper, she adeptly ground the dried ingredients and added them to the stew. Carefully washing the *habas* and *garbanzos*, Catalina placed all the ingredients in the *olla* to begin cooking at sundown in preparation for the Saturday noon meal. The iron pot was placed on the edge of the fire to adhere to Sabbath rules. The aroma of freshly ground spices filled the room.

Energized by cleaning and cooking, the young mother decided to make small pies filled with almonds, herbs and the savory Manchego cheese of Castilla. Stirring the flour, olive oil and egg in the bowl, Catalina mixed the dough and allowed it rest. She portioned out a tenth of the dough and threw it into the fire to burn. This was a Jewish woman's way of thanking G-d for blessings. After rolling the dough out and filling the circular formation with the cheese and herbal mixture, she folded the circle into a half moon and crimped the edges of the *masa* with her thumb to seal the dough. Catalina fried the small pies in olive oil to finish cooking the *empanadas*. The children devoured some pies and then took a short nap.

As Catalina watched the sun beat down on the olive tree outside the door, she reflected on her grandmother sitting under her favorite olive tree. Women needed women to support each other. Sometimes just the action of talking sincerely with a trusted woman confidant opened up a gateway to understanding intricate problems. She confided in her aunt about the priest she encountered at the old synagogue. Her beloved matriarch relayed the oral history of the Inquisition in Toledo and warned her niece of the danger of displaying any Jewish practices in Spain or in New Spain. The Spanish government and the Holy Catholic Church operated as one powerful entity. *Tía* Ana begged Catalina to remember how the Zocodover was used as the designated place to burn Jews pretending to be New Christians.

Reflecting on her visit with *Tía* Ana, Catalina was alarmed to know that the evil priest who confronted her was the nephew of the man who reported Beatriz García to the Inquisition officials. She remembered his bottomless eyes mocking her for being a pseudo Christian. Nervously, Catalina drew the woolen curtains to hide her preparation for the Sabbath. Even though she lived in the country away from others, someone might see a pattern of her Friday rituals.

Tía Ana asked her niece directly about Pedro's faith and behavior. Hearing her aunt voice these words resulted in a torrent of goose bumps running down her arms. Her hands began to sweat. *Tía* Ana persisted in stating her knowledge of a Pedro Robledo being an Inquisition official. Her aunt could not understand this because she knew Pedro descended from the Robledo family from the *Santa María la Blanca Sinagoga*. She wanted to know how Pedro reacted to Catalina secretly following Jewish practices.

Placing a clean silk skirt and blouse on the bed to change into for Shabbat, Catalina fingered the soft weave of the fabric as she realized *Tía* Ana suspected Pedro of being an informant. Little did *Tía* Ana know that Catalina also had come to the same conclusion regarding Pedro. They both suspected Pedro of working for the Inquisition. Pedro held many clandestine meetings with Old Christians and clergy. Something was not right.

Gathering all her children around her, Catalina said to them, "We are good Christians. Our family attends church each Sunday. Your father is respected in the Church and I want to tell you the story of *Las Doce Palabras Retorneadas*. Please pay careful attention to the story because one day you will have to make decisions and you can use this story to make those difficult decisions."

Ana, Luis, Luisa and baby Diego sat on the floor to hear the story. Catalina positioned herself on the simple oak chair, saying, "This is a story my father told me. It is an old Spanish story about a man and his family. Listen carefully to the meaning behind the words."

In an expressive storytelling voice, Catalina said, "Once there was a very poor man with a large family. His wife was with child again and he could not find anyone to be a godfather. Angry, the poor man said he was going to ask the devil to be the godfather. Sure enough, the devil's wife had the son baptized and they named it Twelve and Less. The godparents said they would return for the boy in twelve years less one day.

"The mutual day agreed upon, the devil returned and demanded that the door of the house be opened but the child's guardian angel would not open the door. Finally, the devil said that if someone told him the Twelve Truths of the World that he would not break down the door.

"So the angel told the story by saying, 'The One is God, Christ who came down to bless the holy house at Jerusalem. The two are the two Tables of Moses. The three are the three persons of the Holy Trinity. The four are the four gospels. The five are the five wounds. The six are the six candlesticks. The seven are the seven joys. The eight are the eight choirs. The nine are the nine months. The ten are the Ten Commandments. The eleven are the eleven thousand virgins. The twelve are the twelve apostles. The Twelve Truths of the World are: the Twelve, the twelve apostles, the eleven thousand virgins, the Ten Commandments, the nine months, the eight choirs, the seven joys, the six candlesticks, the five wounds, the four gospels, the three persons of the Holy Trinity, the two Tables of Moses, the One God, Christ who came down to bless the Holy House at Jerusalem.'

"Hearing these words, the devil disappeared and the parents kept their child. And the moral of this story, my children, is: Love and obey the one G-d and follow the Ten Commandments," she counseled the children.

Luisa listened quietly to the story and said nothing. Ana complained about being tired and asked if she could go to bed. All of the children said they were tired and hungry so she fed them more *empanadas*. Before eating, they washed their hands and tried to retell the story in the proper sequence to their mother.

Pedro arrived home exactly at the hour of sunset. He washed himself and smoothed out the wrinkled clothes he wore that day. Then he told her he was extremely tired and was going to bed.

"I made some *empanadas* with almonds, parsley, mint and Manchego cheese for dinner. Would you like to try some before retiring?" asked Catalina.

"No, *gracias, mi esposa*. It has been a long day and I only want to sleep now," replied Pedro as he took off his clothes and went to bed.

Catalina waited until she heard Pedro snoring in bed. He looked tired so she knew that he was sound asleep. She told Luisa and Luis to watch the children while she took a quick walk. Catalina proceeded to the soft caves a quarter of a mile from the house. These caves were similar to the caves near Maqueda. Here, Catalina filled the glass containers with virgin olive oil and new wicks. After having lit the wicks and covering her eyes while she inhaled the smoke of the yellow and blue flames, she recited the prayer of her grandmother:

"Bendito seas Tú, Eterno, Dios nuestro, rey del universo que nos santificaste con tus mandamientos y nos ordenaste prender las velas de la fiesta."

And in the blue flame of the burning candles, maternal mothers with outstretched hands rejoiced noiselessly. Old mothers delighted in Catalina mirroring a tradition of light as a standard bearer of Sephardic heritage.

Rocking herself up and down as she prayed, Catalina prayed silently to worship her G-d in the lonely caves of Carmena that almost touched the earth's uterus. She sighed with relief because she was following the practice of her ancestral mothers as they escaped from Toledo to her physical *conversa* community of Carmena. She felt blessed that Hashem had provided her with such a good and kind husband like Pedro. Catalina petitioned her Maker for her to have more compassion for Pedro because she did not understand him. She prayed that G-d would take them to the New World to Mexico where there would be more seclusion and freedom from suspicious neighbors and vigilant Catholic clergy.

Despite the somberness of hiding to worship G-d on Friday evening, there was a profound joy in knowing that Catalina kept Shabbat. Almost one hundred years after the expulsion of the Jews from Spain, the López women followed what they could remember of the Law. Men were no longer allowed to study in the synagogue. The López women consciously chose to carry on the customs of their mothers and to be the tradition keepers of the home. After all, despite the persecution they suffered for worshipping like their ancestors before them, they were surviving the Inquisition.

In the *villa* of Torrijos, near Maqueda, in 1574, Pedro Robledo initiated his petition for permission to join his first cousins, Miguel de Sandoval and Catalina Sánchez in Mexico City. He specified that he, his wife Catalina, and their children,

Luisa, Diego, Ana and nephew, Luis, be granted passage to Nueva España.

While waiting for approval of the petition of moving to Mexico City, the Robledo family continued with their regular daily lives. Pedro met with peculiar persons of diverse backgrounds at all hours of the day and night. Catalina said nothing about the odd conferences she had observed.

Pedro withdrew even more to himself as the days became weeks and the weeks became months. He began to spend one afternoon each week in Maqueda studying the structure of the castle in the village. The Arabs built this beautiful castle, made of rock, as their fortress. Pedro would walk the border of the grounds trying to memorize the curvatures and lines of the regal edifice of his adored Castilla.

How could he tell Catalina the truth? He was a *familiar* of the Inquisition.[d] As a *familiar*, he was a lay collaborator with the Inquisition. He was given a certificate validating his racial purity and support of the Church and advocacy of the Inquisition. This manuscript entitled him to being exempt from civil authority. To be a *familiar* meant Pedro had to pay an exorbitant fee to falsify genealogy qualifying him as being "racially pure" to hold this position. If this document would assist him in having his family escape from the Inquisition, it would be worth the effort. He would apply for the same position if granted permission to move to Mexico City.

Of course he would never confess to any mortal, especially to Catalina, that his Robledo connections in Toledo stemmed from the intergenerational relationships with the Jewish Cota family. The men of the Jewish families became members of the *Cofradía de Santa María la Blanca* when they suffered from the persecution of *San* Vicente Ferrer in 1391. It was an unspoken bond the men formed to ease the centuries of religious discrimination of their families. He moved to

Maqueda because it was a stalwart *converso* community with strong ties to Toledo. Feeling remorse for having spent so many hours away from Catalina during the afternoon, on one of his walks to the castle, he recalled of his wife's love for roses. In the *patio* of the castle, he found the hardy Persian *rosa de castilla* that the Arabs cultivated with vigor. Cutting the branches having the most abundant blossoms, he carried an armful of roses home with him. As he was leaving the castle, the caretaker asked Pedro if he would like some seeds to plant his own roses. Nodding his head affirmatively, the caretaker handed Pedro a small cloth sack filled with the seeds.

The elderly guardian of the grounds disclosed to Pedro that the seeds were gathered at a special time of the year and was confident the seeds would germinate when planted. Pedro thanked the gentleman for his generosity.

That same evening Pedro gave Catalina the armful of yellow roses. Her face glowed with the joy of receiving the flowers. She put the roses in a large blue Talavera pitcher. The light fragrance of fresh roses drenched the stressed filled air.

As Catalina was arranging the flowers in the container, Pedro told her, "The day we finally leave our *Castilla*, I want you to know that you are more beautiful than the *rosa de castilla* growing in our Maqueda courtyard. Do you see this petal I hold in my hand? There are five heart shaped petals to each rose. Each petal symbolizes my love for you. I loved you when I met you when I was just a lad. Open your hand and let me give you the most beautiful rose. Here, take this sack and put it in a special place. Open your other hand and I will give you the seeds for this flower. If I should die before you, I want you to plant the seeds in our new home and to think of our Maqueda in *Nueva España*. May the Virgin Mary watch over us and keep us from danger. Remember, you are more beautiful than these roses. Do not forget to thank G-d and *Cristo* for all our blessings," he said.

At that moment, there was a loud fluttering noise outside the home. The couple hurried outside to find the reason for the noise. Under the old olive tree by the vineyard, were two golden eagles resting at the trunk of the tree. The eagles were more regal than the symbols decorating the Old Bisagra Gate in Toledo.

As Pedro moved away from Catalina to position himself for a better view of the eagles, Catalina whispered softly:

> *"Herencia de esta vida*
> *herencia de España querida*
> *del Señor en su merced*
> *semos oro de su hesed.*
> *Tú eres mi rosa de Castilla."*[e]

Walking ten paces to be near Pedro, Catalina put her arms around his shoulders and kissed his red and graying hair. She loved Pedro with all her heart.

As she kissed her husband on the cheek, an ocean of doubt crossed her mind. Would her Pedro report her to the Office of the Inquisition? She heard him refer to *Cristo*. Did her husband work for the Holy Office?

Since the conversation with *Tía* Ana, Catalina had abstained from displaying Jewish practices around Pedro. Could she really trust him?

Catalina had no place to go to for refuge. Although she loved Pedro, in medieval Spain, a woman could not abandon her husband. Their marriage through the Catholic Church joined the couple to eternity. If Pedro worked for the Inquisition, what would the powerful Inquisition do to a *conversa* wife?

She would be careful. Catalina knew her Lord was the One and only. She loved Pedro more than her own life but she knew that she loved *Hashem* more. *Tía* Ana was correct to raise the question about Pedro's fidelity.

Studying the lace pattern of the olive leaves, Catalina could almost see her grandmother sitting under the olive tree weighing the relevance of the Tree of Life. One of *abuelita's* favorite sayings was that she herself was *"más vieja que Sara."* Was it her grandmother or was it Sara who Catalina saw sitting under the olive tree?

As the soft wind strummed the olive branch strings, the two golden eagles opened their wings and flew up in the sky soaring above the Robledo home. It was a time for planting. It was a time for learning lessons from the Tree of Life.

Endnotes

a   Blessed are You, HASHEM, our God, King of the
universe, Who sanctified us with His commandments, and has
commanded us to kindle the light of the Sabbath.

b   Your word is a lamp to my feet and a light for my path.
Psalm 119:105.

c   Hordes, Stanley M., *To the End of the Earth, a History
of the Crypto-Jews of New Mexico.* New York: Columbia
University Press, 2005, p.62.

d   *Ibid.*, p. 116.

e

        Inheritance of this life,
        Inheritance of my beloved Spain,
        From G-d in His mercy,
        We are the gold of His loving-kindness.
        You are my rose of *Castilla.*

        Poem by Isabelle Medina Sandoval

Part II
México, Nueva España, 1576 to 1598

1576-1597

México, Nueva España

Catalina López de Robledo

First Generation

Chapter 7

In the year of 1576, the Spanish Inquisition garnered more political strength each passing day. In nearby Ávila, *Santa* Teresa, founder of the discalced Carmelites, was scrutinized by the Inquisition for her stance on mental prayer. *Santa* Teresa's grandfather was a *converso* from Toledo.

Both Pedro and Catalina waited anxiously to hear if they would be able to leave Spain. Rumors of riches and opportunities in the New World reached every little town in the country. However, just like *Santa* Teresa, a nun, experienced hardship with the Inquisition, ordinary persons encountered the same difficulty.

Now a woman thirty some years of age, Catalina learned that the Robledo family was granted permission to leave Spain for Mexico in 1576. Pedro and the family were thrilled about the news. The family left so quickly that there was not time to say goodbye to *Tía* Ana.

Pedro's brother, Alejo Robledo, had requested formal permission to travel to Mexico in 1575. His paperwork was still being reviewed. He hoped to join Pedro and his family soon in Mexico City. It would be wonderful to have family live near them in Mexico.

Pedro had a big lump in his throat when he had to say goodbye to his brother, Alejo. The brothers embraced each other tightly and Pedro hoped Alejo would join the family in Mexico City. Pedro promised Alejo he would try to help him finalize his permission papers.

As the Robledos departed hastily from Carmena, Catalina gazed toward Toledo trying to picture the castle on the hill and the Jewish homeland of her family. As she bit her lower lip to keep from crying, she knew she would miss the olive trees and the mystic smell of jasmine.

Most of all, Catalina would miss her daughter, Ana. Her heart ached for her oldest daughter. Last month, Ana's little ten year old heart just gave out. Her beloved daughter was laid to rest next to the olive tree near the vineyard. With the hectic preparation of getting ready for the trip, even the funeral was put together quickly. She sent her brother-in-law, Alejo, to tell *Tía* Ana about the death. Recovering from a bad cold, *Tía* Ana was unable to attend the funeral.

With one last glance back at Carmena, Catalina looked at the olive tree. In the leaves of the olive tree she saw bright silhouettes of a grandmother, mother and a young girl. She realized the figures were her grandmother, her mother and Ana. Wiping tears away from her eyes, she looked back a final time and saw a fourth figure. She knew by the brightness of the light that it was Sara.

A feeling of comfort came over her. Catalina prayed the *Shema:*

"Blessed are You, HASHEM, our God, King of the Universe, Who forms light and creates darkness, makes peace and creates all."

Pedro paid some men to assist the family take their few belongings from Carmena to Sevilla. The Robledos were eager about the trip and realized that they had to be one cohesive family unit to be successful. The family traveled through the great city of Madrid and finally arrived in Sevilla. Approaching the city, a blood orange moon like the tart citrus fruit of Sevilla danced over the immense Guadalquivir River emptying into the Atlantic Ocean. Catalina heard her grandmother tell stories of many Jews leaving Sevilla in 1492 because of the expulsion. People said that Christopher Columbus was detained on his epic voyage because Jews were waiting on the ships in the harbor ready to journey to any country willing to take them. The expulsion coincided with *Tisha B'ab*, the day of fasting, to commemorate the destruction of the First and Second Temples. Grandmother said there was much crying because the expulsion signified the destruction of Spanish Sephardic Jews.

Storks and pink flamingos flew near the waterways. Intricate black fancy iron grill work decorated the homes. The lush *patios* of the city were adorned with ceramic pots filled with scarlet red geraniums. As a gateway to the New World, Sevilla was a magnificent cultured port city teeming with life and opportunity.

The market place near the Giralda sold fascinating products. Beautiful books, rich textiles, Arabic medicines, pottery painted with gold and the finest wines of Spain could be purchased on the plaza. American products of tobacco, cocoa, tomatoes and vanilla were for sale at the right price.

Before boarding the boat, Pedro insisted on visiting the Cathedral of Sevilla to pray for a safe trip. Catalina gasped to see the amount of opulent gold covering so many saints and altars inside the immense cathedral. She heard all the gold came from the New World.

The laborious voyage across the tempestuous Atlantic Ocean was difficult and bumpy. En route to the New World, swaying jolts of the ocean waters were similar to the ups and downs she had encountered in her own life. When they finally reached land, she vowed to Pedro that she only wanted to live in a quiet home far away from neighbors and people.

The boat finally landed in Vera Cruz. It was a welcome sight to see the tropical port city and to walk on firm ground. After resting from the boat ride for a few days, Pedro hired some men to escort the family to Mexico City.

Arriving in Mexico City after a tiring trip, the family was awed by the vitality of the cosmopolitan area. Massive geometric stone pyramids landscaped the country. The Natives of Mexico City secretly revered their god, Quetzalcoatl, known as the plumed serpent. The Spaniards destroyed the Native temples and built Christian churches to replace the old religion. Natives practiced their religion in secret to hide from the Spanish priests.

Pedro asked Spanish officials where he could find his first cousin, Catalina Sánchez, and her husband, Miguel Sandoval. No one knew his cousin. Pedro was confused because he had counted on living with Catalina while establishing his household. He had to verify this relationship with the civil authorities. All the required paperwork was in order. Pedro was troubled about his cousin. He was also panicking about how he was going to provide for his big family.

On the boat ride from Sevilla to Veracruz, Pedro became friends with Tomás Sánchez, a native of Santander. This new friend, a wealthy miner with a home established in Mexico City, invited Pedro and the family to stay with him until he could find his cousins or find a job. Pedro contacted Tomás and the Robledos were guests at the Sánchez home for several weeks.

To make the best out of the complicated situation, Pedro decided to take his family to see the city. The Robledo family rode the boats of Xochimilco meandering through the canals decorated with exquisite tropical flowers. The roses and geraniums of Spain paled in comparison to the color and superb flowers of New Spain. World travelers they met claimed that the waters of Xochimilco were more breathtaking and cleaner than the boat excursions in Italy. Wild birds of brilliant plumage lived in this luxuriant tropical habitat of Xochimilco. While riding on the boat, out of nowhere, luminous iridescent feathers soared through the sultry air and darted into the dense foliage.

The *mercado* was the largest place of exchange she had witnessed. Fragile bright flowers were for sale everywhere. Indians sold a food similar to the *empanada* which they called a *tamale*. Instead of using wheat for the dough, corn was used to cover a hot red chile and meat combination. The corn mixture that covered the chile and meat concoction was wrapped in a big green plant leaf and steamed until the dough was cooked.

The children and Catalina were addicted to the fresh chocolate beverages sold in the *mercado*. Each member of the family drank a cup of exotic fresh chocolate each day. Comparing the market of Mexico City to other markets, the markets of the Zocodover in Toledo and Sevilla were small and limited in products. Gold and silver were plentiful and Mexican products were exchanged for metal coins.

As the family toured Mexico City, the great culture of the Aztec civilization was evident in the majestic architecture of pyramids and communal buildings. However, the missionary priests were occupied with Christianizing the Indians and converting the buildings into churches. Catalina recognized how the Natives were forced to convert to Catholicism and she empathized with their spiritual pain. It was not right for the Spanish religion to kill the intangible spirit of the soul.

Much to Catalina's surprise, she discovered she was pregnant. Pedro knew he would have to find work quickly to support his growing family in a strange land. Tomás Sánchez gave Pedro some good leads for mining jobs. It was a new country and there were many opportunities for eager immigrants.

Pedro was unable to find his cousin. With Tomás' generous assistance, Pedro did find a job. In hope of striking it rich with mining, Pedro moved the family from one mining place to another town. Catalina gave birth to a daughter, Francisca, en route to Cimapán. Because Pedro was literate, he translated documents for the mining operations. Catalina gave birth to her son, Alonso, in Cimapán in central Mexico in 1577; to Pedro in Temazcaltepeque in 1578; and to Francisco in Zamora in 1579.

Changing residences so frequently in mining towns and having four children in five years, made Catalina want a permanent residence she could call home. She missed *Tía* Ana and was saddened to discover that her aunt had died in 1579. Pedro's hair had turned completely gray and it took him longer and longer to get to the same distance.

The cities of Toledo, Sevilla and Mexico City did not appeal to Catalina. As beautiful as Mexico City was, she longed for the peace and quiet of a small town. Pedro was fortunate to find work in the mines. Pedro heard from his mining friends about a new colony to be established far north of Zacatecas. He discussed the new possibility with Catalina. After a long discussion, the couple decided that they had already traveled one ocean, many deserts and were still looking for the home of their hearts. Yet Catalina wondered if Pedro really had a cousin by the name of Catalina Sánchez. No one in Mexico City knew her. This appeared very strange to her.

Catalina sensed that the actual reason for the family moving was due to the burgeoning power of the Inquisition. The intensity of the Mexican Inquisition started on November

4, 1571 by *Don* Pedro Moya de Contreras exercising his powers as Chief Inquisitor. Rumors circulated that church officials were searching all cities and small towns to enforce Church regulations regarding heresy. For some reason, Pedro was always near Inquisition officials before a problem surfaced. Catalina could not help but see a pattern evolving around Pedro and persons being reported to church officials. This loyal wife, deep in her soul, could not and would not trust her husband.

The purpose of the Holy Office was to eradicate Judaism and heresy from the Spanish Empire. Starting in 1589, in the Americas, the Inquisitors were cohesively persistent in ferreting out Jews or Judaizers. As the fervor of the strength of the Mexican Inquisition heightened, Pedro appeared to become more aloof.

In 1596, the king of Spain was concerned about Jews living in New Spain. As a result of this royal interest, the Inquisition focused on Luis Carbajal, a native of Portugal. His uncle was governor of Nuevo León. The first public display of the clout of the Inquisition became apparent to all citizens when Luis Carbajal and his sisters, after a long trial, were sentenced in 1596 and were burned at the stake in Mexico City. This precise setting mirrored the same burning at the stake scenes the Robledos heard family members discuss that they had witnessed in Toledo.

Catalina first heard from her friends about the recent exploration party north of Zacatecas led by Gaspar Castaño de Sosa, a close friend of Luis Carbajal. Sosa was born in Portugal and was living in San Luis, Nuevo León when he decided to make the exploratory excursion. To the citizens of Mexico, Portuguese was a synonymous word for crypto-Jew. As Lieutenant Governor and Captain General of Nuevo León, Sosa spearheaded the expedition in Nueva Vizcaya from 1590-91. Under the Laws of Settlement of 1573, it was alleged that many of his 170 colonists were known Jews and crypto-Jews. Castaño de Sosa was arrested on charges of illegally attempting to colonize what later became New Mexico. He was exiled to China and murdered en route during a mutiny of galley slaves in the Moluccas. After his death, his case was reviewed and he was exonerated by the High Court.

Information of Sosa's expedition spread throughout the mining areas of the province. Word disseminated among the crypto-Jews that a new land of milk and honey, past the deserts, past dangerous Indians and located in isolated mountains, was a choice settlement for colonization. This new place was almost two thousand miles away from Mexico City.

Catalina overheard several conversations in the plaza that Jews could hide in safety further north in rural areas. Inevitably, the comment was made that the priests were vigilant of Jews of unclean blood contaminating the good Catholic people.

Catalina and Pedro spent hours discussing their various options of joining colonists now ready to embark on this journey under the leadership of Juan Pérez de Oñate. Pedro was already sixty years old. Would his health endure? They had sacrificed so much to leave Spain and their families in La Mancha. Pedro still dreamed of walking around the castle of Maqueda and being near his family. Surely he was not meant to spend his last days working the mines and inhaling the fine dust in his lungs. And *pobrecita* Catalina. She was a weaver and had only a small loom with little wool to weave the items of her heart. Besides, they were still very much in love and they wanted to enjoy the last days of their lives together.

However, in the deepest chamber of her heart, Catalina still wondered if Pedro might report her to the Inquisitors. She believed he loved her very much and he appeared to be happy. Yet it seemed that with each move they made, another neighbor was reported to the priest for heresy. Catalina reflected on the punishment of the *conversos* in Mexico City. Although she was troubled by Pedro reporting her, it was worth a chance to move away even further from the Holy Office.

Pedro reminded Catalina of the *rosa de castilla* seeds he had given her and told her that he wanted her to plant them in their own courtyard. He spoke of the two regal golden eagles sitting beneath the olive tree. His voice quivered when he talked about his Ana being buried near the olive tree in Carmena. His voice sounded sentimental and it was evident he was still looking for a place to call home.

Catalina told her husband that in this season of their lives that they had survived the Spanish Inquisition and had experienced living in a New World. She promised Pedro she would plant the roses in the *patio* of their new home. In a way, Catalina thought the rose of Castile was similar to planting the roots of the Jewish faith. It was a time to think about planting.

1598

Santa Bárbara, Mexico

Oñate Expedition and Settlement

Catalina López de Robledo

First Generation

Chapter 8

*D*on Juan de Oñate y Salazar was an ambitious man with a strong desire to lead others. Although he was funding the New Mexico expedition, he negotiated with *Don* Luis de Velasco, viceroy of New Spain, before signing the contract. Spain would definitely profit from the colonization by increasing her land and gaining new citizens.

Oñate's father was Cristóbal de Oñate and had a reputation of providing dependable and courageous leadership. A wealthy man, Cristóbal owned many stamp mills in silver rich Zacatecas. His wife was *Doña* Catalina de Salazar y de la Cadena, a native of Granada, Spain.

Oñate agreed to equip and arm two hundred men serving both as soldiers and colonists. He would be given the title of *adelantado* and further requested that the titles be passed down to his heirs. He would receive an annual government salary and had the exclusive power to make land grants and award the title of *hidalgo*. In addition to these conditions, the contract provided for Oñate being placed under the Council of Indies, the king's chief advisory council in Sevilla.

Despite the outward appearance of being confident and eager to lead the settlers north, Oñate was consumed with doubts. Would the soldier-colonist be of substantive caliber to fight in a heroic manner if this were truly needed? There was no known route for this large expedition. Would he guide this group on a safe road? Could he provide and care for these people? Oñate, in the epicenter of his soul, knew he would do his personal best. His honor was at stake.

On December 22, 1597, Juan de Frías Salazar, under the power of the holy sign of the cross, administered an oath to Juan Pérez de Oñate. Friar Salazar made a thorough governmental examination pursuant to regulations of persons and all their possessions making this northward expedition. Interest grew steadily each day during the month of January 1598.

Settlers were required to be Catholics in good standing. Colonists were excluded for the expedition if they had expressed an interest in Protestant, Muslim or Jewish beliefs to others. All men living a minimum of five years in the frontier of New Mexico were promised the title of *hidalgo,* the lowest rank of nobleman. Men talked animatedly about making the trip to earn this title of nobility.

Some settlers seriously considered the implications of making such a long journey. Spaniards living in Mexico City were usually wealthy and frequently purchased products brought by the ships of Europe and China. By traveling far away from Mexico City, what substantive contact would there be with other citizens? New Mexico was thousands of miles away from Mexico City. Where could settlers purchase the quality supplies they needed?

Literacy was viewed as an integral component of Spanish culture. In 1553, the Royal and Pontifical University of Mexico established an institution and process for conferring bachelor and advanced degrees in theology and law. Education and literacy were valued within the New World culture. Citizens of the Spanish Empire witnessed government and church officials read and write formal documents on a daily basis. Literate officials and citizens would respond or communicate in written Spanish. Priests and nuns recorded all relevant church activities in their registers and read from their books during services. Inquisition officials read proclamations, recorded testimonies, trials and investigations. Literacy was of utmost importance to women and men in Spanish society.

Among the colonists, males and females were trying frantically to decide what to take with them to a place so far away that they knew that they would probably not return to the secluded Santa Bárbara, Zacatecas outpost. All items had to be transported to New Mexico by cart. The *carreta* was constructed entirely of wood and pulled by a yoke of oxen. A cart was made and the sides were covered with wagon bows supporting a cloth cover made in Michoacán. The cart was attached on top of two wooden wheels made from a single section of cottonwood with no iron or hardware fittings used in the construction. The legal load each *carreta* could carry was approximately two tons. The cart was replicated after the same model used in southern Spain; the usefulness of the humble cart was of imperative importance to the colonists.

Difficult choices had to be made on what to take on the trip. Some affluent colonists took velvet, Chinese taffeta, cordovan slippers, silk stockings and fine linens. Other colonists packed the bare necessities to enable them to endure the dangerous journey and unknown obstacles along the desert and pine covered mountains of the unknown lands. Some colonists weighed the practicality of taking staple items like woolen blankets, sturdy leather shoes and metal utensils. Each family decided what they needed most and packed the carts accordingly.

Colonists making this journey knew they would probably never return to Mexico again. These brave persons included the following:

Pablo de Aguilar, Ascencio de Archuleta, Dionisio de
Bañuelos, Juan Benítez, Juan Gutiérrez de Bocanegra, Juan
Pérez de Bustillo, César Ortiz Cadimo, Juan Camacho, Esteban
Carbajal, Juan de Caso, Bernabé de las Casas, Juan Catalán,
Gregorio César, Juan Cortés, Marcos Cortés, Pedro Sánchez
Damiero, Juan Díaz, Juan Pérez de Donis, Felipe Escalte, Juan
Escarramal, Marcelo de Espinosa, Marcos Farfán de los Godos,
Juan Fernández, Manuel Francisco, Álvaro García, Francisco
García, Marcos García, Simón García, Luis Gascón, Bartolomé
González, Juan Griego, Francisco Guillén, Antonio Gutiérrez,
Gerónimo de Heredia, Antonio Hernández, Francisco
Hernández, Gonzalo Hernández, Pedro Hernández, Antonio
Conde de Herrera, Cristóbal de Herrera, Juan de Herrera,
Alonzo Núñez de Hinojosa, León de Isati, Diego Landin,
Francisco de Ledesma, Juan de León, Domingo de Lizana,
Cristóbal López, Juan López, Alonso Lucas, Francisco
Márquez, Gerónimo Márquez, Hernán Martín, Juan Martínez
Juan Medel, Alonso Gómez, Baltazar de Monzón, Juan Morán
Diego Núñez, Juan de Olague, Cristóbal de Oñate, Juan de
Ortega, Regundo Paladín, Simón de Paz, Juan de Pedraza,
Simón Pérez, Juan Pinero, Francisco de Posa y Peñalosa,
Alonso de Quesada, Francisco Guillén de Quesada, Martín
Ramírez, Juan Rangel, Pedro de los Reyes, Pedro de Ribera,
Alonso del Río, Diego Robledo, Francisco Robledo, Pedro
Robledo, Sebastián Rodríguez, Bartolomé Romero, Moreno
de la Rua, Juan Ruíz, Lorenzo Salado, Juan de Salas, Alonso
Sánchez, Francisco Sánchez, Antonio Sariana, Juan de Segura,
Francisco Vaca, Francisco Vásquez, Jorge de la Vega, Juan
Velarde, Francisco Vido, Juan de Victoria Vido, Gaspar Pérez
de Villagrá, Juan de Zaldívar, and León Zapata.

As was the Spanish custom of documenting events, copious governmental records and lists were made. The Robledo family was included in this listing. Luisa Robledo, daughter of Pedro Robledo and Catalina López, was recorded as the wife of Bartolomé Romero, a soldier with the expedition. Bartolomé Romero wanted to keep his own documentation and had started his own recordkeeping. Luisa Robledo watched her husband write the entry of the family in the journal he was keeping for himself. In beautiful Spanish script, he wrote:

Ensign Pedro Robledo, 60 years old, native of Maqueda, son of Alejo Robledo, of good stature, with gray-hair.

Diego Robledo, 27 years old, native of Maqueda, son of said Pedro Robledo above of good stature, red beard.

Alonso Robledo, 21 years of age, son of Pedro Robledo, native of Cimapán in New Spain, of good stature, red beard.

Pedro Robledo, 20 years old, son of Pedro Robledo, native of Temazcaltepeque, of good stature.

Francisco Robledo, 18 years old, son of Pedro Robledo, native of Valladolid in New Spain.

And I, Ensign Bartolomé Romero, 35 years old, son of Bartolomé Romero, native of Corral de Almaguer, of good stature, swarthy, black beard. My wife is Luisa Robledo, daughter of said Pedro Robledo.

Two days outside of Santa Bárbara, Father Cristóbal Salazar gave permission on January 26, 1598, for *Don* Juan de Oñate to guide the lead wagon toward New Mexico from the San Géronimo River. The official records listed 170 families and 230 single men forming the expedition. Accompanying the families and men were ten Franciscans, eight priests and two lay brothers. Twenty clergy provided spiritual support and church guidance to monitor the 400 person party.

As the colonists moved in a northerly course, directly behind the expedition followed eighty bulky *carretas*, 1,000 cattle, 3,000 sheep, 1,000 rams, 100 black cattle, 150 colts, 150 mares and 1,000 goats. This impressive caravan snaked for four miles making from five to six miles in one day. This road traveled was named the *Camino Real*, the royal road from Mexico City to Santa Fe.

The Robledo and Romero *carretas* traveled next to each other. This physical proximity gave Luisa and Catalina ample opportunities to converse and share the experiences as adult female colonists with one another.

"*Mi hija*, light of my life, do you have your embroidery with you? It will be a long trip and this project will help you use your time wisely. I am so happy you are using the *sabanilla* I wove for you to embroider. I saw my mother and her grandmother in Toledo embroider the *colcha* stitch the way their mothers did for the elaborate altar cloths and textiles they made," commented Catalina to her daughter.

"Si, *Mamacita*, I have everything right here in this wooden box. I am working on the Tree of Life design you drew for me in the dirt of Carmena before we left Spain. I recall you telling me that the women in our family have stitched this design for many years," replied Catalina.

"Yes, my precious. The design will be beautiful in your new home. Soon you and Bartolomé will have children and this design will mean more to your family in your own home," said Catalina.

Steadying herself from the jerky cart ride, Luisa reached inside the white box and displayed the indigo blue handspun wool flower embroidered in the couching stitch to her mother. "You are so wise, *Mamacita*," remarked Luisa.

"I am not so sure about your choice of calling me "wise" my dear. Do you know that *Don* Juan de Oñate's wife is the direct descendant of *conquistador* Hernán Cortés and his wife, Isabel Moctezuma? Isabel Moctezuma is the granddaughter of the late Aztec emperor. She is a beautiful, wealthy and gracious woman," said Catalina.

"No, I did not know that," replied Luisa. "However, I did hear from Bartolomé that *Don* Juan de Oñate's maternal ancestors were Jews from Spain."

"Oh, my, this is news to me. G-d willing, we will all find a time of peace in our new homes," added Catalina.

"Yes, I heard his mother's family descends from the Halevi family in Burgos. This Halevi converted from being a rabbi and took a Christian name. Someone said *Don* Juan is more devout than most Catholics because he wants to hide the fact that his family is Jewish. Do you know anything about this family?" asked Luisa.

"Hmm, Halevi, I remember my grandmother mentioning this name. I heard Halevi's Jewish wife converted to Catholicism many years later, just before she died. She was a faithful Jewess as long as she was able to keep her faith," replied Catalina.

Looking intently into her mother's eyes, Luisa commented, "I am sad that Halevi's wife had a stronger faith than her rabbi husband. What about my father? Do you think he watches you? I think it is quite odd that crypto-Jews are interviewed by Inquisition officials after *Papá* has befriended them. What do you think?"

Catalina was caught off guard. She did not expect her daughter to articulate the thoughts of her soul. Brushing the lint off her skirt, the mother replied, "I have to admit I have been suspicious of your father and his role with the Inquisition. However, he is my husband and he is your father. Until I have absolute proof that he is involved with the Inquisition, I must support him. Truthfully, what choice does a *conversa* woman in our culture have? I depend on him to provide for my children and me. Without your father, I would have to depend on my sons and my daughters. I do not want to be a burden to my children. I love your father very much. Do I trust him? This is the unanswered question."

The reality of Catalina's words whipped the women like the sudden cold breeze disturbing the settlers. The mother added, "Can you believe we have been on the caravan for almost three weeks? The sun is warm at times although it is January. However, compared to Santa Bárbara, it is colder here. From what I hear from others, it will be colder in New Mexico. I enjoy feeling the warmth of the sun hitting my face. That cold wind though makes me wonder about fall and winter. Dearest daughter, night is closing in on us and soon the wagons will stop for the night."

The awkward moment addressed the question of a loved family member betraying Jews and possibly his own family. Within a few minutes, the sunlight faded rapidly.

Catalina and Luisa said good night to each other. Luisa embraced her mother warmly. Her mother was correct; women were an extension of their husbands. The touch served as a physical gesture of the love the daughter had for her mother.

The evening sun was beginning to set and the heat of the Chihuahua desert suddenly turned cool. A poppy colored cloud bellowed in the sky and dissipated slowly into a light gold shadow finally disappearing in the azure dusk of the night to come. There were three hundred miles of this stark desert to cross until water could be replenished at El Río Grande. Water was being rationed and the colonists discussed the perils and hardships of having to travel such uninviting country.

Then they reached a stretch of dry waterholes, and the shortage of water became critical. A thin coating of dust covered the wagon and bodies of the sojourners. Water was so scarce that personal use was not permitted.

On March 10, 1598, the Spaniards traveled through present day Chihuahua. They found a small stream of water they called the Río Sacramento because it was discovered on Holy Thursday.

Thankful for finding the stream of water, Oñate ordered the expedition party to stop. A temporary chapel was constructed for worship. Priests and men prayed on their knees. Then the soldiers whipped their backs with scourges. Oñate left the group to lash his back in privacy.

Catalina observed the service objectively. As she recited the Christian prayers automatically, she was reminded of the devout Spanish penitence during Holy Week. In the darkness of the altar, she saw the shadows of Oñate and his ancestor, Solomón Halevi, rejecting the holy bread of *San* Vicente Ferrer. All three men were scourging their backs with the passion of Jewish anguish. She blinked her eyes to confirm what she saw. This time, she saw only the cross on the altar.

The water quenched the physical thirst of the colonists. There was enough water to bathe and wash clothes. The priests had an adequate supply of holy water to administer to all. There was always a worry of not having enough water and rationing the little water they did have. Colonists wondered if they would survive in this desert. But this lack of water did not help Catalina's dehydrated soul. She needed to refresh her soul and felt there were too many eyes watching her.

Luisa opened her small white wood box she purchased at the *mercado* in Mexico City. She unknotted the blue handkerchief and touched the detailed damascene work of gold and silver etched in the fine steel. Luisa became aware last year that *Doña María de Adeva*, the woman who gave her the brooch near the family's former synagogue in Toledo, was actually the mother of her husband, Bartolomé. From her husband, she learned that the Adevas were Benadevas, Jews from Sevilla. The Adevas moved to small town outside of Toledo from Sevilla when their home was destroyed by the *menudos.*

The entire world was small indeed. Luisa remembered the powerful light of *Shekinah* shining on the three females near the old synagogue of her family. Little did Luisa know that she met the matriarch of her future husband...was there no rest allocated for her? She was hiding in Toledo, she hid in Mexico and she was still hiding now. What was this new colony going to bring? Would she find rest in the new settlement?

At the same moment, Catalina was opening her white box of keepsakes. She caressed the cloth bag containing the rose seeds Pedro gave her. Her heart rejoiced knowing that with each turn of the wheel of the *carreta* that she and Pedro were closer to finding their final home in the new land of great opportunity. In the corner of the box she found a small bag filled with some other seeds. She opened the bag and found the lavender seeds from Carmena. Catalina had forgotten about the seeds when she placed them in her bags when they left Carmena. These were the seeds she planted to grow lavender for Ana's tea. She would plant these seeds to make tea for her grandchildren. She could almost see her Ana sitting next to her. She would plant the rose and lavender seeds when she moved into her new house.

It was a time to build a new home; it was a time to start a new life. It was a time to leave the wilderness.

1598

La Toma, Province of New Mexico

Catalina López de Robledo

First Generation

Chapter 9

Recognized as one of the last known *conquistadores* of the Spanish era, Juan de Oñate, knight in armor, directed his expedition further northward. Having started at the most northern outpost of Santa Bárbara, the expedition progressed steadily further each day. Oñate and his colonists were influenced by the ideal of the Spanish patron saint, *Santiago*, Saint James the Apostle, depicted as the knight on a white horse fighting for Christianity. The expedition was guided by the common mission of colonizing new lands for the Crown and Church.

On April 19, 1598, the caravan came to a total halt because the cart wheels would not budge on the sand. The heavy *carretas* required dirt for traction and were unable to propel adequately on the yellow sand particles. *Don* Juan Oñate divided the caravan into two sections. He used the draft animals in the back of the caravan to be double-hitched to the *carretas.* This extra power provided the energy needed to move the *carretas* across the sands.

Finally, they reached the Río Grande. After successfully traveling over the treacherous sand, *Don* Juan Oñate declared a celebration of thanksgiving for the colonists. People prayed, laughed, rested and rejoiced over their good fortune. After the long trek through the desert, animals and humans were ready to replenish their supplies and rest their bodies. The colonists rested for a week while hunting and fishing along the plentiful Río Grande.

Catalina decided to spend one day washing the dirty clothes. Late in the afternoon, while Friar Salazar was on his walk, he saw Catalina hanging her clothes along the willow branches of the Río Grande. Friar Salazar, a cousin to Juan de Oñate, created the opportunity to talk to Catalina.

"*Doña* Catalina," he began, "you are one of the most pious women on this caravan. You pray with such sincere goodness and your devoutness is apparent to me. You remind me very much of my maternal side of the family. What is your native city?" asked Father Salazar with seemingly innocent curiosity.

Hiding her curly long gray hair in a loose bun under her shawl covering her head, Catalina responded, "I am a Toledana and have lived with my husband Pedro near Maqueda for over half my life. Twenty years ago we decided to come to *Nueva España* and find the home of our dreams. Now Pedro is the oldest enlisted soldier on this expedition. I am proud to say that all of our four sons are serving King Phillip on this expedition. I realize I am old enough to be a grandmother and I am most happy that my children can make a new start in a new land."

"*Doña* Catalina, please do not take offense for what I am about to say," interrupted the priest. "Please listen to the meaning of my words. In spite of your devoutness and zealous display of your love of our Holy Catholic faith, something is not quite right. I have observed that religious Catholics often hide behind their profound devoutness. Would you please explain to me why I sense something is not right?"

Transported back to the cobblestone streets of Toledo, Catalina was again involved in the spiritual warfare of another Catholic leader. Friar Salazar was regarded as arrogant and petty. Pedro referred to the priest as *alzado* because he presented himself to others as powerful and believed all others were inferior.

Carefully selecting her words, she answered, "Friar Salazar, I really do not know what you are talking about," answered Catalina in her most demure tone. She felt her heart pounding furiously under her gray dress.

"Please, I am old enough to be your son. I may be young, yet I am troubled. During our recent days of our blessed *Semana Santa*, I witnessed you declining to take the Holy Communion. I have observed you wait for stars to appear on Friday before you start your prayers. Am I wrong? I know what I have seen," stated the priest.

"What may I add? I do not know why I may do these things; they are old practices I saw in Toledo. I thought faithful Catholics did these things. I am a good Catholic," retorted Catalina as her mind was leaping through vast canyons of logic from the generations of her mothers in Toledo to answer the priest with wisdom and truth. At the same time, she wanted to go untouched by the jails and fires of the Inquisition, the same powerful institution that burned her Jewish relatives in the Zocodover. She could feel fatal fear leaping like hot flames in her throat as she struggled to form the words to answer the priest.

In a calm tone she replied, "I am truly devoted to my Catholic faith. When I open my eyes in the morning, I immediately sing the *Canto del Alba*. Let me sing some verses for you.

> *Aquí viene el alba*
> *Aquí viene el alba*
> *Cantemos todos*
> *Ave María.*

> *Cantemos el alba*
> *Ya viene el día*
> *Daremos gracias*
> *Ave María.*

Nace el alba María
Y el Ave tras ella
Cantemos todos
Ave María.

Cantemos el alba
Ya viene el día
Daremos gracias
Ave María.[11]

"Do not be afraid, *Doña* Catalina. I am not going to report you. *Don* Juan and I descend from the family of Salomón Ha-Levi of Burgos. I do caution you to take extreme care in being more private about your observances. Carbajal women in Mexico City died for their crypto-Jewish practices and many others await their sentencing. Be careful. Many ears and eyes hear and see all. This is my only advice to you," responded the priest in a tender manner.

"I am a good Catholic woman, Friar Salazar. I do appreciate your advice and will refrain from following old traditions of infidel practices. Please have a good day. I have much laundry to wash," said Catalina as she ended this emotional conference.

With a tear in his eye, Father Salazar brushed away the light covering of the pale yellow dust from the banks of the Río Grande from his forehead. He blinked his eyes several times. Then he looked at Catalina. His blue eyes were as cool and cold as the distant water of the Río Grande. "May your *neshama* find peace," replied the priest as he walked away from her heading back to the camp.

Turning his back to return to the camp, Catalina watched the priest leave. Father Salazar told her to find peace in her soul. Why did he not say *alma* instead of using the Hebrew word *neshama* for soul?

As Catalina heard the crunching sounds of Father Salazar's sandals receding through the cottonwood twigs of the grassy bank, she felt her heart pounding with the worst terror she had experienced in her life. Her mind raced fearfully with being taken back to Mexico City and being imprisoned by the Inquisitors. Would she be burned at the stake? What about her children? And poor Pedro, he was sixty now and his color did not look good. Her neck was covered with heavy perspiration. What would Friar Salazar do? Did she throw him off track with her answer of being a good Catholic? The next few days would reveal her destiny. Just what season was it?

Touching the hand wrung clothing on the willow branches to test for dryness, Catalina stopped to rest. It was hard to keep clothes clean on the trip. As she washed the clothes with lye soap, the water would mix with the fine sand and turned into a light mustard yellow color. This sun would dry the clothes and help bleach them white again.

Unexpectedly, a warm familiar hand stoked her head. She turned around and felt herself being drawn into Pedro's arms. He kissed her tenderly and told her how much he loved her.

Reaching inside his shirt, he pulled out a *bota* of wine from Sevilla. He motioned for her to sit down next to him on the spring grass overlooking the clean waters of the strong river. They laughed and took turns squirting the red wine into each other's mouths.

Pedro held Catalina to his chest. They saw magnificent virgin country. Across the riverbank stretched the bright majestic white sands swirling into the dry mountains and eventually draping the hills with fine alabaster crystals. Dotted in the opaque sands were cacti called yucca plants stretching six feet in height and five feet in width. This month of April, the plant emitted a four foot slender stalk filled with three inch ivory cascading bouquets. The gentle wind swayed the yuccas in classical movement to an original thanksgiving musical composition of the Río Grande tempo.

"Look, Catalina, see how the yucca tells us that we are royal? I do not even need the title of *hidalgo* any more. King Solomon did not have such splendid fans in his royal kingdom. Only the heavens know that we are lovers forever," laughed Pedro as he pulled his arm tighter on Catalina's small waist.

"Ay, Pedro, there has never been any other man in my life since the day I met you in our homeland of Toledo. I wish *Tía* Ana had not died because she would be so happy to see us now. Sometimes I think our lives are nothing more than the forgotten burned candles of our Carmena. I love you more than the day I married you. I know it has been difficult for you to leave our beloved Spain to make a new life in a strange world. We live in such a tumultuous world. Now you are a *conquistador* in this new province. You know that I will always love you, *mi querido,*" she whispered.

"Have you kept the *rosa de castilla* seeds I gave you from the castle of Maqueda? It is the rose of our homeland. The only flower more beautiful than the *rosa de castilla* is you, my *rosa de castilla.* Your yellow petals of goodness are worth more than gold. By G-d's love and mercy, He gave me you. My love for you is strong and nothing will ever separate us," he emphasized as he planted a kiss on her cheek.

"Pedro, I bought a white box in Mexico City to keep the rose seeds you gave me. When we build our home in the land of New Mexico, people from all over the world will come to see the bright flowers of our Maqueda. You are part of my soul, *mi amor.*" Her voice quavered as he stroked her hand.

With the wind force of a thousand thunderbolts of lightening quivering in space, two golden eagles flew over their heads and disappeared in the *bosque* of the river. The colonists called the vegetation along the Río Grande "the forest" because it reminded them of the dense greenery of home.

The husband and wife looked up in the big turquoise sky to see the two eagles soaring directly above their heads. It was the second time they saw two golden eagles together. They said nothing and felt the magic of the moment.

The silence was broken by the frank question Catalina was asking Pedro, "My husband, I have something serious to ask you. The last time I visited with *Tía* Ana, she asked me if you were a *converso* or if you worked for the Inquisition. I have been afraid to ask you this question. Seeing the two golden eagles again, has given me the strength I need. It does not change my love for you. I want to know for myself what you really represent. Only you can answer this question for me," she pleaded with her husband for an honest response.

The two golden eagles were perched together high up on the boughs of the immense cottonwood tree. A purple throated hummingbird darted above their heads.

Clearing his throat several times, Pedro quietly spoke, "Catalina, you and I are like the two eagles we see. We are mated forever. Do you really have to know? I believe my life reflects my beliefs. Why do you ask? Yes, I was a *familiar* of Toledo. I asked for this position from Inquisition officials to take us out of the hotbed of fear in Toledo. I am a son of the Jewish Robledo family. We were forced to convert a full century before the Alhambra Decree. The Robledo men became members of the *confradía* to hide our *converso* ways. I married you because I knew the López family was *converso* too. I have never said anything to you because I have this intense fear that the Inquisition will harm us. Maybe I am too mature. Maybe I am too tired of keeping this inside me. Do you not know that I love you because you keep our traditions? I decided to move us to New Mexico because I was very afraid that the Inquisition would find us out. I want our children to survive. Do you not know why I love you? As the mother of our children, you are the Toledo tradition keeper of our family."

Stroking her hand, he whispered in her ear, "You are my soul's mate and we will always be together. Even if one of us

leaves the other one behind, the living one will find a sign of the
rosa de castilla. You will always feel the magic of our love. The
rose represents the flower of our *converso* faith of Spain."

Looking deep into Pedro's hazel eyes, she replied, "If I die
first, you will hear the roses sing:

> *Herencia de esta vida*
> *herencia de mi España querida*
> *del Señor en su hesed*
> *semos oro de su merced.*
> *Tú eres mi rosa de castilla.*"[b]

She placed her soft hand on the temple of his graying hair
and vowed, "You, *mi amor*, are the *conquistador* of my heart.
Tía Ana's favorite saying was: *Cada oveja con su pareja.* You
and I are the *converso* sheep of La Mancha. Out of the darkness
of the Spanish Inquisition, we symbolize the Sephardic legacy
of *El Eterno.*"

Tears welled in Pedro's eyes as he held Catalina's hand.
Pedro and Catalina remained at their special place until the sun
turned into a Granada pomegranate silky flower in the sleeping
sky. As the retiring sky changed from red to *rosa de castilla*,
they held hands and walked back to the caravan to seek their
private home in the new province.

Tomorrow was another day and this night was a time for
loving.

On April 30, 1598, about twenty-five miles below the present
city of El Paso, Texas, *Don* Juan de Oñate named this location
La Toma. A formal ceremony was held to take possession of the
land in the name of Spain. Shots were fired in the air. Trumpets
were blown and the royal silk banner of King Phillip was waved
in the air. At noon on April 30, New Mexico formally became a
province. It was a time for change.

1598

Robledo, New Spain

Catalina López de Robledo

First Generation

Chapter 10

The refreshing vacation along the Río Grande invigorated the colonists. A positive physical and mental transformation had taken place. The livestock had an opportunity to rest, eat wild vegetation and drink water. The camp environment was lively and a spirit of hope vibrated through out the community.

This unknown road from Mexico City to Santa Fe was later called *El Camino Real,* also known as the Royal Road. On this road across isolated deserts and mountains, real dangers of lack of water, persons, snakes, insects, greed, faith and jealousy lurked in every camp. The volatile weather often changed at a moment's notice. At times intense heat, snow, hail, cold and wind thwarted daily travel. Geography and weather were problematical hindrances for each person making this treacherous journey.

Since reaching La Toma, the colonists felt a communal sense of security. They took advantage of this vast source of food and water. Meanwhile, the colonists nurtured a community of friendship. They helped each other and often listened to the nightmares, hopes and dreams of their friends. They became *comadres* and *compadres* because they shared the same experiences.

During the campfire talks in mid-May, men discussed how their lives would change once they became *hidalgos.*

One colonist defined this word as meaning *hijo de alguien.* With this title, like other nobility in Castile, the nobleman did not have to pay taxes and had the right to use the title of *Don* before his first Christian name. During recruitment efforts, New Mexican colonists were enticed by the promise of this title by Juan de Oñate. As colonial dreams became reality with the geographical closeness to their destiny, speculative talk about their titles and fortunes was a favorite evening time conversation.

On May 20, Catalina decided to host a dinner for the Robledo family. Luisa and her husband contributed wine from Mexico, the four sons brought the fresh fish they caught in the river and Catalina prepared whole-wheat *torta amarilla,* similar to the *torta blanquesa de Toledo,* on the griddle of the campfire. This wheat flatbread was always a welcome dish. As always, like her female ancestors before her, she tore off the dough for the first *torta* and threw it in the fire. Francisca, her other daughter, helped her mother cook.[c]

The family laughed and joked with one another all night long. The brothers played the guitar and sang the *romances* of Diego's native Spain. Diego had to play his mother's favorite melody, *Una Nina en el Balcón,* because it was her grandmother's favorite song. The song described the love of a shepherd and a maiden.

Sitting on a big rock near the warmth of the campfire, Diego's nimble hands played the cords of the song on the guitar. He sang:

"*Una niña en un balcón le dice a un pastor, Espera*
que aquí te habla una zagala que de amores desespera.
No me hables de esa manera le responde el grande vil
mi ganado está en la sierra con él me voy a dormir.
Te doy una pila de oro y tres cañas de marfil
tan solo porque te quedes esta noche aquí a dormir.

No quiero tu pila de oro ni tus cañas de marfil
mi ganado está en la sierra con él me voy a dormir.
Mira que lindos cabellos y llevarás que contar
el sol se enamora de ellos cuando me siento a peinar.
Mira que pulido pie para un zapato dorado.
Mira que soy niña tierna y que estoy a tu mandado.
No me hables de esa manera le responde el grande vil
mi ganado está en la sierra con él me voy a dormir.
Te doy las mulas y el hato el catre y el almirez
tan sólo porque te quedes esta noche y otras tres.
No quiero mulas ni hato ni el catre ni el almirez
mi gandado está en la sierra con él me voy otra vez.
Mira pastor aturdido no me quieres entender
me dejas con mi vergüenza cuando te empiezo a querer
a la vuelta de tu viaje no vas a saber que hacer.
Zagala, dueña de mi alma zagala vuelvo a venir.
Zagala, cuando me hablates tus palabras no entendí.
Perdóname gran señora si en algo yo te ofendí.
Cuando quise, no quisites y ahora que quieres no quiero;
pues llora tu soledad que yo la lloré primero.
Mira zagalita hermosa dueña de mi corazón
perdóname esta faltita que tu siervo es el amor.
Cuando quise no quisites y ahora que quieres no quiero;
pues llora tu soledad que yo la lloré primero.
Haré de cuenta que tuve una sortijita de oro
y que se cayó en el mar y así la perdí del todo.[d]

Finishing playing the ballad, Diego looked up at the family members surrounding him. Pedro's eyes were almost closed and Luisa was yawning. As he paused for a moment, Catalina broke the silence and reminded everyone that all needed their sleep and it was time to go to bed. The mood was light and friendly; the family gathering was uniting and joyful. The music reminded the family of the times they spent together in Toledo and Mexico.

Catalina woke up the morning of May 21. As was her daily habit, she said, *"Modah Ani,"* and thanked G-d for returning her soul. Immediately, she sensed something was not right. Washing her hands and combing her hair back into a bun, she went to look for Pedro because she did not find him in bed with her.

She called his name and he did not answer. Then she saw Pedro curled up in a blanket near her sons sleeping on the ground. Tapping his shoulder, she tried to waken him. He did not respond. Catalina grabbed his hand and felt the chill of death surround her.

Holding Pedro against her bosom, tears of Carmena watering the *rosas de castilla* and their joint home that was not meant to be, washed down her cheeks in agony. As her heart was breaking, one golden eagle perched on the nearby cottonwood, flew away to the shelter of the river. At that moment, she knew her *amor* would not leave her.

Suddenly, Luisa was by her side and was crying. Francisca heard the sobbing and comforted her mother and sister. Both sisters woke their brothers up to tell them the sad news.

This was a time for dying. Before washing Pedro's body with river water, she prayed:

"Te rogamos, Eterno, Tu Ley es verdad.
Darnos ánimo y fuerza."

Catalina bathed Pedro's body with supreme care starting from his head and working down to his feet. She used the warm water to clean her husband's body for his final journey. As she washed his feet, she realized Pedro would never stand on the ground of their new home or smell the yellow roses.

From her white box, Catalina took out one pearl from Mexico and placed it inside his mouth. Then she stitched some white *sabanilla* into a small bag and put the dirt from

Carmena she had placed in her container for burial purposes. She positioned the white bag of dirt inside Pedro's clean linen white shirt he would carry with him when he was laid to rest. At least he would have his precious soil from Carmena cushion his last journey.

The news of Pedro's death spread throughout the camp. The first colonist's death was a shock to the group. Tears flowed and gifts of thoughtfulness and kind deeds were provided to the Robledo family by the other colonists.

Friar Salazar conducted a service for Pedro. He stated that Pedro was a native of Toledo, Spain. The friar added that Pedro would be missed by his wife and all his children as well as by the members of the expedition. He blinked back a tear when he said, "Pedro was a spiritual man of Toledo, respected by all for his spirituality."

It was a time for weeping.

Pedro was buried where he died. This campground was named La Cruz de Robledo. Today, this site, on the *Camino Real*, became the landmark for the south entrance to *La Jornada del Muerto*. The colonists named the bluff overlooking the grave site *Robledo Mountain*. This isolated mountain, 5,890 feet high, marked the final resting place of the Toledo Spaniard. His grave rested between the river and the bluff.

Eagles were known to fly over this mountain. Some said that the golden eagles belonged to the old Spaniard. A wooden cross was placed on his grave by his daughter, Luisa. His son, Diego, carved a rose on a marker. As the mourners left the graveside, one golden eagle circled overhead.

Catalina went though the motions of trying to put her life back together. She washed and cooked like she had done before Pedro died. The joy in her heart was gone. Her life dream of having a real home with Pedro disappeared at his death.

The expedition had to continue the journey to the north. As the caravan was approaching near the Indian pueblo of Santo Domingo, Catalina saw two eagles flying above her. She knew Pedro had not left her. She went to her carved white box and held the seeds Pedro had given her in Carmena. As she held the seeds to her heart, she promised him that she would plant the seeds at her house and would wait to see the roses bloom.

This was a time for mourning. It was a time to grieve for the *converso*.

Endnotes

a   Here comes the dawn
Here comes the dawn;
We all sing
Ave María.

Let's sing the dawn
The day is coming;
Let's give thanks
Ave María.

Here comes the dawn
Here comes the dawn;
We all sing
Ave María.

Let's sing the dawn
The day is coming;
Let's give thanks
Ave María.

b   "Inheritance of this life,
inheritance of my beloved Spain,
from G-d in His mercy,
we are the gold of His loving-kindness.
You are my rose of *Castilla*."

c   An olive size piece of dough must be separated and
burned for each batch of dough for *jalá* or *torta* as required in
the Torah.

d   A young girl on a balcony says to shepherd: "Please
wait for here a shepherdess calls and she is desperate for love.
"Do not speak to me that way," the boorish rustic responds,
"my flock grazes in the mountain, with it I'm going to sleep.
I'll give you a pile of gold, and three reeds of ivory
if only you'll deign to stay, and sleep in my room tonight."
"I don't want your pile of gold, nor your reeds of ivory
my flock grazes in the mountain, with it I'm going to sleep."
"Just look, what beautiful hair, and you'll have a tale to tell;
the sun falls in love with it, whenever I'm combing it.
Look what a delicate foot, proper for a golden shoe.
See what a tender child am I, and that I'm at your command."
"Do not speak to me like that," the boorish rustic responds,
"my flock is in the mountain, with it I'm going to sleep."
"I'll give you the mules and ranch, the bedstead and the brass
mortar,
if only you'll stay with me, this night and another three."
"I don't want your mules nor ranch, nor the bed nor the brass
mortar;
my flock grazes in the mountain, to it I'm returning now."
"Look here, you bewildered shepherd, you don't want to
understand;
You leave me with my dishonor, just when I'm starting to like you;
When you return from your trip, you will not know what to do.
"Shepherdess, love of my soul, shepherdess, I'm back again.
Shepherdess, when you spoke to me, your words I
misunderstood.
Please forgive me, noble lady, if I have offended you."
"When it was my wish, you would not, and now that you wish,
I do not,
so weep in your solitude now, as I wept in mine before."
"Look, my beautiful shepherdess, dearest owner of my heart,
forgive me this trivial fault, for love is your faithful servant."
"When it was my wish, you would not, and that you wish, I do not;

so weep in your solitude now, as I wept in mine before."
"I shall imagine I had, a ring of gold for your hand,
but it fell into the sea, and thus I lost it forever."

Espinosa, Aurelio M. and J. Manuel Espinosa, ed. *The Folklore of Spain in the American Southwest.* Norman: University of Oklahoma Press, 1990, pp. 88-90.

e   "We beg you HASHEM, your Law is truth. Give us courage and strength."

Part III
Oñate New Mexico
1598 to 1680

Summer 1598

San Gabriel, Nueva Vizcaya

Catalina López de Robledo

First Generation

Chapter 11

ince Pedro's death, the days were blurred by
fragmented recollections of the daily miles traversed
on the expedition. Over thirty years of marriage
had carved many memories of Pedro in Catalina's heart. Now
Catalina found herself alone. Her four sons and two daughters
were of invaluable comfort to her.

Before the Robledos left the town of Carmena belonging to
the Duke of Maqueda, Pedro had to secure statements from his
neighbors about his character. Citizens in La Mancha described
Pedro and his wife as "honorable and essential." Indeed, although
Pedro was never to be called *Don* Pedro, he was a man of honor.

Continuing in a northerly direction, the scenery changed
from cracked dry desert mountains to soft indigo mountains
laced with pink and red mesas. The nights and mornings were
cooler with each passing mile.

The caravan reached Santo Domingo on June 30. Along the route, Oñate met with Native leaders to seek advice as to where to establish the permanent colony. Natives frequently advised him to proceed to *Yunge* and *Okhe*, approximately twenty miles north of present day Santa Fe.

On July 11, 1598, the pioneers arrived in the scenic enchanting valley. On this day, twenty-two years prior to the founding of Plymouth Rock by the English, *Don* Juan de Oñate established San Gabriel del Yungue. Oñate negotiated with the San Juan Indians to allow his party of four hundred persons to reconstruct some old ruins.

A week-long festivity to celebrate reaching the final destination was held. The play, *Los Moros y Cristianos,* was performed for the Natives and colonists. The point of the play portraying the Moors and the Christians was to accentuate the supremacy of Christianity over all other faiths. Because few citizens in Europe were literate, plays served an educational tool in educating the audience. Citizens were able to comprehend basic spoken language; however, formal education, inclusive of writing and reading, was generally reserved for the wealthy and upper class. The Church used the play as a teaching strategy to inculcate Catholic dogma.

The genuineness of actually living in San Gabriel jarred Catalina out of her mourning for Pedro. She had to unpack her things because she had reached her destination. After living near the castles of Spain and the pyramids of Mexico, reaching this new destination launched her into another reality. She was living in a mud apartment in the high mountains over a thousand miles away from the nearest mining outpost. Looking out at all four directions around San Gabriel, serrated mountaintops were covered with snow. What would winter unfold in this aloof terrain?

The Robledo sons knew the living arrangements would be difficult for Catalina. The Spaniards would reside in the abandoned pueblo. The colonists reconstructed the rooms into small living units. Some rooms were for sleeping only and other units were modified to accommodate copper griddles to bake wheat flatbread or had firepits dug in the floor for cooking.

The Pueblo women were kind and willing to help. Catalina asked Blanca, a young Native mother with two young boys, to help her. In turn, Catalina gave Blanca food for her assistance.

Blanca helped Catalina make a firepit in her room. This fire hearth of rock allowed Catalina to cook for her family. Blanca was an asset in helping clean and prepare the room for living. Chests of Puebla pottery were organized for daily use and the prized teapot from the Zodocover was kept in storage. The teapot was in perfect condition after the trips across the Atlantic Ocean and the 2,000 mile journey along the Camino Real.

The settlement was taking definite shape as a cohesive community. There were three levels to the colonial plaza and it was a neighborhood separated by apartment walls. The lack of privacy because of the close proximity of neighbors for every moment of day and night taxed each pioneer. Confidential conversations were often heard by adjoining occupants.

Diego was astute to perceive that his mother was lonely and missing Pedro. He doted on his mother and worried about her quietness. Returning home from riding horses on a military assignment with his brother-in-law, Bartolomé, Diego decided to speak to her.

Entering her room, he observed that she was drinking hot tea in an attractive white Native cup decorated with striking black geometric designs. "What are you drinking?" he asked his mother.

"I am drinking some *hierbabuena* tea Blanca gave me," answered Catalina. "She says it grows along the *acequia* and she dries it for teas. It is almost as good as the Moroccan tea *Tía Ana* made in Toledo. Would you like a cup of tea, *mi hijo?*" she asked her son.

"Muchas gracias, pero no. I wanted to come by and see how you are feeling today," said Diego.

"G-d was good to give me another day of life my son," she replied while opening the white wood box to smell the lavender seeds. "Last month, on a warm September day, I took some of the rose seeds your father gave me and planted them along the sunny side of the plaza near the river. I hope the seeds take. It is cold and freezing but I still hope that they will grow in spring. I gave your sister, Luisa, the rest of seeds for her to plant when she makes her home. We are not even in a home now and live in small rooms next to each other. I miss the plains of Maqueda and the scent of the yellow roses. I also miss the lavender flowers; I always think of my sweet Ana."

"Do you remember the yellow roses? Aunt Ana would pick the flowers and put them in the blue graceful vase made in Talavera," asked his mother.

"I barely remember seeing some yellow flowers at the castle in Maqueda," Diego replied as he stroked the red beard on his chin. "It was so long ago that is seems like a dream to me. In a way, San Gabriel reminds me of Spain because we live in the country. I do miss all the fresh olives and the rich vineyards filled with sweet purple grapes," he said. "I am happy you planted these flowers. I trust they will grow in spring and then we can bring them into our homes like we did in Toledo," answered Diego.

Diego reached over to Catalina's small hand and held it. Nothing was said and the touch linked the mother to son.

"Mamacita, you know that I love you. I wish I could be near you more but I have to assist *Don* Juan with the military visits to many pueblos. Let me ask you something. What do you think of me setting up your loom in this room? You can card the wool of the *churro* sheep we have in the *corral.* Would you like me to put up your loom now?"

"Ay, mi Diego precioso, you have the heart of my *Tía* Ana. I will have so many projects to make. I will weave *jerga* for

the floors just like they did in Toledo. I will weave clothes and even *sabanilla* for the *colcha*. We need new linens and the *sabanilla* is the best fabric to use. Thank you my son," Catalina responded warmly.

Diego left his mother's room to retrieve the loom. He knew weaving would take the pain out of her loneliness and her projects would fortify the warmness of the room.

December crept into Yunque like an insulating frigid blanket of eighteen inches of river ice casing the settlement. Two feet of snow covered the ground and the pine trees were brushed with thick white sparkly hand blown frozen crystals. Catalina had become accustomed to eating the indigenous beans and chile. She could not weave enough *sabanilla* to warm the cold she felt chilling her deep inside.

She watched for the three first stars of Friday night and then went to church to pray. The Yunque evenings were most beautiful nights she had ever witnessed. The stars were so close that she could almost touch them.

As a mother, she agonized over her sons. All of her young sons were hardly home. It was rumored that the Natives wanted the colonists to leave their Pueblo lands. Her daughters, Luisa and Francisca, spent most of the day with their mother. The daughters tried to keep their mother busy by talking, sewing and cooking.

A week before Christmas, Catalina inventoried the pantry to see how much flour there was in storage to make *buñuelos* for Christmas. This delicacy was always made in her childhood home. Her *abuelita* told her that the pastry was made to celebrate *Hanuka,* the celebration of lights. Integrating this bread with a variety of other dishes never raised one suspicion from any outsiders. It was her way to keep the Toledo tradition of her mothers. In her home, Catalina defied royal and church mandates to be a standard bearer of her customs.

Francisca barged into the room crying, "I cannot believe it. Tell me it is not true, *Mamacita*. Please tell me it is not true."

Placing all attention on her sensible Francisca, she said, "I have no idea what you are asking me..."

An unexpected knock at the door stilled the quietness. Opening the door, she saw *Don* Juan Oñate himself standing before her. Why was he here?

He removed his metal helmet with the long red plume from his head. Bowing from his waist, he said, "Doña Catalina, please excuse this interruption. As you know, we have had difficulty with the Indians. My nephew, Juan de Zaldívar, Commanding General, and eight soldiers were killed at Ácoma. I regret to inform you that your son, Pedro Robledo II, died in a fall. Your other son, Francisco, survived. Please accept my sincere condolences."

Catalina thanked *Don* Juan. He bowed again and left the room. Catalina then held Francisca and they both cried profusely. At least her husband lived a good life of sixty years. How could her son be dead? He was a mere lad of twenty years of age. Her heartache suddenly changed to the proportion of the pain of a hole of the size of a pomegranate. She felt nothing but sorrow penetrating her heart and then let out a loud wail.

Oñate and his soldiers went back to Ácoma. After the February 1599 trial, Native males over twenty five years had a foot cut off with a chisel and were placed in slavery for twenty years. Males from twenty-five to twelve years served twenty years of servitude. Women over twelve served twenty years of servitude and sixty young girls were sent to Mexico City to live in a convent with the condition they would never return to home again.

It was a cold season for all citizens. It was a season when Native and Spanish tears froze in their eyes with the iciness of the times.

By the end of summer of 1599, a few of the seeds from Maqueda had taken root in San Gabriel. No one knew why this Catholic settlement was named San Gabriel. Catalina's grandmother told her that Gabriel was an angel positioned near the Tree of Life.

Catalina heard some more sad news. Fray Cristóbal de Salazar, *Don* Juan's nephew, died at a place near Robledo where Pedro rested. Fray Salazar was headed back south to recruit more colonists for the San Gabriel colony when he died. The Spaniards named the location *Paraje de Fray Cristóbal*. She felt a twinge near her cheerless heart. This priest was a trusted clergyman and he kept his word. From him, she learned to be careful and not demonstrate practices that would direct attention to her. She prayed for the young priest that he would rest in peace. She felt better knowing Pedro rested close to the friar.

May of 1601 descended like a diminutive dried bouquet of flowers. Little rain fell in spring and the earth was begging for moisture. A few yellow roses bloomed on the branches of Pedro's rosebush.

Stooping over to inhale the rich fragrance, memories of Maqueda and Pedro inundated her soul. She recalled Pedro telling her how the five petals of the rose would symbolize his year of jubilee when he had turned fifty.

Cutting off a rose with her right thumbnail, Catalina placed the rose under her nose and smelled the scent she had not smelled in twenty years. With her index finger, she outlined the petals of the flower. For the first time, she saw how the petal formed a perfect velvet heart. It was a time to set Pedro free. It was also a time to remember the *converso* faith of Spain. The living rose symbolized Jewish faith.

Catalina placed the rose on her heart and thought of Pedro, Ana and her son. She put the rose on her heart again and thought of *Tía* Ana and the *juderías* of Spain. She placed the rose on her heart one more time and asked Hashem to remember to have

Luisa's baby growing inside her womb to keep the traditions of her grandparents from La Mancha.

Within the next few days, women flocked around the wall to see the rosebush. Some women took cuttings and others said they would wait for the seeds to mature. Within the decade, the yellow rose grew near many of the homes and *acequias*. The dried rose petals were used for medicine and perfume.

A drought started in 1601 extending into 1602. Great care was given to using all food wisely and not wasting as little as one bean. In winter of 1602, Luisa gave birth to a healthy baby boy. Bartolomé and Luisa named him Bartolomé II. He was the first native child born to the family of the new settlement of San Gabriel. A beautiful boy with olive skin, the baby had auburn hair. The Romero and Robledo families loved their son.

Luisa and her husband held their child together. Bartolomé II was the first son of the first generation to be born in Nueva Vizcaya. The Romeros were content knowing that they both left Spain and were living in the new lands of the Spanish Crown.

Preparations were under way to have the baby baptized. In February, the boy was taken to the church for his baptism. The perfunctory ceremony was lovely and the baby did not cry when water was poured over his head. This was a definite good sign and the priest was delighted with the baptism. After the ceremony, family and friends gathered for a treat of hot chocolate and *bizcochitos*. Catalina baked the cookies in one of the *hornos* in the plaza.

After the guests left, Luisa, Bartolomé, Francisca, Catalina and the Robledo brothers remained in the room. Catalina had a fresh pitcher of water on the small table. All relatives gathered around the baby.

Captain Romero held his son in his arms. The newborn *criatura* was placed in a blue ceramic bowl Catalina brought with her from Maqueda. The lukewarm water was poured into the bowl. Dipping the new *sabanilla* cloth in the water, Catalina scrubbed the baptismal oil and water off the head of the baby. His head was washed several times to remove all traces of the Catholic sacrament. As was the custom of the *conversos,* coins were thrown into the baby's bath water. Catalina prayed that an angel would watch over Bartolomé for the rest of his days on this earth.

Francisca poured wine into the plain small cups Blanca made for the special occasion. It was a time of joy that the families celebrated jointly. Diego, the proud uncle, reminded guests of how his mother taught the family in Carmena to worship one G-d and follow the Law.

The remainder of the afternoon was spent sharing the good fortune of having a new baby in the family. He was passed from one relative to another and loved by all.

Luisa whispered to her mother that she wanted to walk outside to the top of the hill overlooking San Gabriel. She told Catalina to dress her baby warmly.

Catalina looked surprised and Luisa asked her mother, "Do you remember when I was a little girl that you took me to the old synagogue in Toledo? I have not forgotten that day and I had this deep longing to know who my people are. Later that day, my future husband's mother went out of her way to see us and gave me the gift of the pin. This is one of the most special memories I have. It was meant to be that Bartolomé and I would be husband and wife."

Hugging her mother and her baby, Luisa added, "I became aware at that moment that I am a Jewess and that I am only one generation beyond you and my two beyond my grandmother. You and your mothers before you provided silent support and spirituality for me. Family is important and blessings from *Hashem* are important to me. I watched you suffer silently through the years but your faith has always remained strong. You would honor me by walking to the top of the hill and holding your grandson, Bartolomé, while I chant this prayer I wrote. Please join me," she pleaded, while taking her mother's hand in her hand.

Catalina stammered, "Y-Y-You have the soul and the wisdom of our Toledo mothers. You follow the customs of the *conversas.*"

In forty-degree weather, at five o'clock in the evening, the two women, with a baby wrapped tightly in the woolen blankets Catalina had woven for him, walked to the top of the hill, far away from anyone.

When they reached the top of the pine-covered hill, Luisa asked Catalina to hold Bartolomé up in the air while she chanted her prayer, she called "A Mother's Prayer" a gift to her son. In a lucid profound liturgical voice springing from her soul and the souls of her mothers before her, she chanted:

> *"Señor Most High*
> *Father of my life*
> *Here in the mountains*
> *of New Mexico*
> *I ask you for blessings*
> *for my child.*
> *Señor I belong to you.*
> *Señor I belong to you.*
> *God of Abraham*
> *God of Isaac*
> *God of Jacob*
> *God of this mother*
> *God of Israel*
> *God of this world.*
> *Señor I belong to you.*
> *Señor I belong to you.*
> *that my children*
> *and their children*

will have a good life.
My children belong to you
And our dreams belong to you.
Señor I belong to you.
Señor I belong to you.
Praised be the Eternal.
Do not forget us
so far from our family
so far from my Padre
Señor I belong to you.
Señor I belong to you.
Long live our King.
Long live our Law.
Long live Adonay.
Señor I belong to you.
Señor I belong to you.
Long live our King.
Long live our King.
Long live our Law.
Long live our Law.
Long live Adonay.
Long live Adonay.[n]

When Luisa finished chanting, she anchored her arms on her mother's strong arms and they held Bartolomé together. Catalina had tears of joy flowing down her cheeks. It was a blessing of three generations to worship *Hashem*. They were surviving the Spanish and the Mexican Inquisitions. It was a time of light in the darkness. It was a time for beginning a new life.

1607

Gabriel

Catalina López de Robeldo

First Generation

Chapter 12

Lámpara es para mi pie tu palabra
y luz para mi senda

Your word is a lamp to my feet
and a light for my path

Psalm 119:105

Gabriel shook his head. From Toledo to the alien lands of Mexico and Nueva Vizcaya, Catalina, like Naomi, moved from her home to live in a new land with her husband. Like her grandmother, this meek woman pondered the words of her youth.

Catalina received the meaning of sacred words she heard in her upbringing. She often thought about her grandmother comparing the olive tree to the Zohar's Tree of Life. Although she did not study the formal written word, she modeled the oral tradition of the word she received.

One day while tending her roses, Catalina clutched her chest and fell over on the ground. When Luisa found her mother, she found Catalina with two yellow roses in her hand. Luisa ran with incredible speed for help. When she returned to the rosebush, two golden eagles watched Luisa and Diego from the nearby *piñon* tree.

As she had seen her mother do when her father died, Luisa prayed the same prayer of over her mother,

"Te rogamos, Eterno, Tu Ley es verdad.
Darnos ánimo y fuerza."

Luisa prepared her mother's body for the funeral. Starting from her head and working her way to her mother's feet, Luisa sadly gave her last gift to her mother of administering the final body preparation for her burial. She gently washed her mother's body with new *sabanilla*. As she washed her mother's calloused feet, she wept recalling all the private conversations they shared and the talks that would never be voiced again.

From her mother's white box, Luisa took out the last pearl from Mexico and placed it in her mother's mouth. Then she stitched Catalina's white *sabanilla* into a small bag and placed the last dirt from Carmena inside her mother's clean white blouse.

Luisa, whose Jewish name was Lucía, saw the white light surround her mother. She recognized the light from Toledo where she stood with two women in front of *Santa María de la Blanca Sinagoga*. Lucía saw the identical light encircling her mother. The *Shekinah* from the heavens extended to the New Mexican desert. This was proof that Catalina used *Adonay's* words to be the light of her pathway.

All of a sudden, Luisa knew why she was named Lucía. Her task was to be a light and to use *El Eterno's* oral Torah in all aspects of her life.

Catalina would have a fine funeral in the Holy Catholic Church. A *velorio* and rosaries would be said for this humble woman of Toledo. Today, though, in the blinding white light shining on her body, Catalina reached the final Gate of the Tree of Life. It was a time for light in the darkness of the bleak Inquisitions.

1655

Santa Fe

Catalina Romero de Telles Xirón

Fifth Generation

Chapter 13

Viceroy Juan de Mendoza y Luna, Marquis of Montesclaros, accepted Juan de Oñate's resignation in 1608. Oñate was accused of serious offenses ranging from extreme cruelty to the Indians, execution of deserters and submission of false reports relative to mineral wealth.

Oñate's wife, *Doña* Isabel Moctezuma, died at the family home in Pánuco in 1620. In an attempt to clear his name, Oñate went to Spain and appeared before the Council of the Indies to make his case. In 1623, the king granted Oñate reimbursement of the 6,000 *peso* fine for his conviction of the New Mexico offenses. He was still banned from New Mexico.

Although recognized for his contributions to Spain, Oñate for the remainder of his life served as the mining inspector for all of Spain. Punished for his offenses of cruelty, Oñate brought with him the concept of the *rancho* and livestock to the Southwest and he was the masterful engineer of the *Camino Real*. He requested that his remains be transferred to a chapel at the *Colegio Imperial* in Madrid.

In 1610 the authorized government headquarters was moved from San Gabriel, twenty miles south, to a new place called Santa Fe. New Mexico was designated as a royal colony by the Spanish Crown. Pedro de Peralta was appointed as the new governor of New Mexico in the new City of Holy Faith.

In 1492, in a small town named Santa Fé, wedged between the magnificent Alhambra palace and the snowy peaks of the imposing Alpujarra Mountains, King Ferdinand and Queen Isabel issued the Edict of Expulsion banishing the Muslims and Jews from Spain. Perhaps the name of Santa Fé was chosen by Governor Peralta in New Mexico to emulate the rudiments of the Catholic foundation on a new continent.

In the new settlement of New Mexico, on the surface, good Catholics obeyed Spain and the Holy Catholic Church. Yet in mid 1650 Mexico City, María Rivera, a crypto-Jew, said to the Inquisitors that to observe *La Ley de Moisés*, it was necessary to "flee to the ends of the earth"...and this would have included the colony of New Mexico, over thousands of miles north of Mexico City, and even closer to the unknown end of the world.[b]

Since 1610, the *villa* of Santa Fé had grown into a prosperous town. Several times during the year, caravans from Mexico City brought mail, supplies and linked the colony to Mexico. Other persons and soldiers joining the original settlers included the following surnames: Abendaño, Baca, Chávez, Domínguez de Mendoza, Durán, Fresqui, Gallegos, Mondragón, Olguín, Ortega, Pacheco, Padilla, Salazar, Serna, Tapia, Telles Xirón, Trujillo, Valencia, Varela Jaramillo, Vásquez, Vera and Zamora. As more persons moved into Santa Fe, friendships and social interactions helped the new city develop into a valued community.

The Romero family also grew and contributed positively to the community. One Romero young lady attracted the attention of many eligible suitors. A stunning beauty at fourteen years of age, Catalina had long black hair and translucent beige skin. Underneath her thick black eyelashes, a pair of emerald eyes glistened. Only five feet tall, her energy was contagious. She was the daughter of Josefa Archuleta and Sargeant Major Bartolomé III, prominent citizens of Santa Fe.

Bartolomé III was beyond thrilled the day Josefa gave birth to his daughter. He always wanted a daughter; women were regarded with high esteem and respect in the Romero household. Catalina Robledo, the maternal matriarch from Toledo, was venerated in his family. His father gave him the white box Catalina bought in Mexico to store her treasures. When his own daughter was born, he and Josefa named their infant baby girl, Catalina López Romero, in honor of her ancestral grandmother. Since birth, his daughter displayed a high degree of independence, strength and fortitude. Older family members often commented that the Sergeant Major's daughter had the same eyes as his Toledo grandmother, as well as the same kindred spirit.

The Romeros were respected in the Santa Fe community. Sergeant Major Bartolomé's father, Captain Bartolomé II, was born in San Gabriel, distinguishing himself in the military. Along with *Don* Juan de Oñate, soldiers including Captain Bartolomé II, engraved their names at El Morro. This site was located on Zuñi land on a two hundred foot sandstone butte. The Spanish inscription read:

There passed by here the Governor Don Juan de Oñate from the discovery of the Gulf of California on the 16th of April, 1605.

Loyal and dedicated soldiers of the Spanish Crown, the Romero and Robledo families served their country with distinction. Honor and military distinction were important to these families.

Notwithstanding military honor, and renown for civil leadership as an officer, Bartolomé III, prized his family as his most important part of his life. He adored his wife, Josefa Archuleta. Catalina was the delight of his life. His daughter was like the fresh *rosa de castilla* blooming each spring that Catalina López de Robledo carried with her from the realms of Castile.

Her eyes were as colorful as the juniper of Santa Fe and her character radiated like the gold quality of the yellow roses. She was known in Santa Fe as *Doña* Catalina. Several years passed and a handsome Spanish soldier from Mexico City came to serve in the military in Santa Fe. This soldier, José Telles Xirón, like many other young men, was taken by Catalina's extraordinary beauty. As he sought opportunities to be at church or in the plaza when she was known to frequent such social events, José managed to court Catalina. She would swirl her ivory and black lace fan while flirting outrageously with him. Her green eyes were almost bewitching. Then she would toss her silk black Chinese shawl with the long fringe over her shoulder to reveal a beautiful rounded feminine shoulder.

José was a handsome young man. Almost six feet tall, his slender build in his fitted soldier's uniform certainly intrigued Catalina. His skin was milk white and his hair was onyx black. When he walked, he carried himself in a confident and balanced manner.

It was obvious to all in Santa Fe that these two persons were deeply in love. José finally decided to approach Bartolomé Romero and ask for Catalina's hand in marriage. Although he was most nervous to speak to the respected officer, José found his courage and asked Sergeant Major Romero for permission to marry his daughter. Catalina's father said that José would have to come by his house the following morning while he thought overnight about this serious marriage proposal. The father would also speak to his daughter and his wife about the situation. If José found *calabazas* outside the door of the house, then the marriage proposal had been rejected. If there were no pumpkins outside the house, then this meant Bartolomé had given his permission for José to marry Catalina. This was an old Spanish custom the Romeros and Robledos practiced in La Mancha.

Bartolomé stipulated that if the marriage proposal were accepted, that José would follow the traditional Spanish custom of paying for the entire wedding. The groom would also be responsible for paying for the bride's trousseau. The love stricken officer agreed to pay for these items.

José, with a huge lump in his throat, was up early the next morning to see if his marriage proposal had been accepted or rejected. He was anxious as he approached the Romero home situated near the plaza. As he looked intently at the entry door of the home, to his delight, he saw no pumpkins outside the Romero house.

After the formal *prendorio,* Catalina and José were married. Catalina loved her husband just as her ancestral grandmother had loved Pedro Robledo. They became best friends. Even after marriage, when Catalina fanned her black lace fan, José's heart sizzled with all his being. Her haunting eyes intoxicated him to the point of psychological inebriation.

Without one doubt, they were the most handsome couple in the Santa Fe area. From the date of the exchange of their wedding vows, the couple produced several children in rapid succession. Their sons and daughter were handsome and beautiful like their parents.

Bartolomé was close to his daughter and grandchildren. He would tell his *nietos* the story of *Las Doce Palabras Retoneadas* emphasizing the Two Tables of Moses. He had taught Catalina to attend Mass since she was a small child and to display an intense love for the Catholic Church and the teachings.

Catalina grew up a devoted Catholic and never missed Mass, even attending services when she was not feeling well. When Catalina had been ten-years old, her father had told her that he was a *converso.* His grandfather was Bartolomé Romero and his grandmother was María Adeva, both of Corral del Almaguer. The Romeros were New Christians and the Adevas were originally Benadevas, Sephardic Jews from Sevilla.

Catalina begged her father to teach her how to say the Friday night prayer. She had been cautioned by her father never to reveal any family secrets to anyone under any circumstances. When others were not looking, in the privacy of her home, she lit two candles on Friday night in the back room of the house, which had no windows. Her father taught her the Spanish prayer for lighting candles.

When Catalina prepared *tortillas,* she always discarded the *masa* of the first *tortilla* because she knew it could not be eaten by anyone. She washed off the baptismal water from her children after the baptism by the priest. She asked that a guardian angel would watch over her newborn child. She changed her clothes every Friday and watched for the first three stars in the Friday night sky to measure the beginning of *sábado.* She did what she had seen her mothers and their mother do before her. Intuitively, an invisible force deep inside her, guided her to follow these traditions. Meanwhile, a nagging fear haunted her about not displaying any of these traditions in front of anyone except her parents because she might be reported to church officials.

Catalina followed another Toledo custom of the family. On the first day of January, she recorded the weather pattern for twelve days. For example, if January first were a snowy day, then January for the year would be snowy. She recorded the weather for the next twelve days with the thirteenth day representing the reversal pattern for December working backwards to January. She referred to this custom as *cabañuelas.* This weather forecasting provided a system for predicting the annual climate. Her father told her that he believed the practice originated from the Jews of Toledo, celebrating a *fiesta.*

José Telles Xirón had the two *encomiendas* of San Felipe and Cochiti. His duty was to guarantee the spiritual and temporal welfare of the Natives of San Felipe and Cochiti. This Spanish practice translated into the Natives paying tribute to the *encomendero* each May and October with local products. José had the reputation of being fair.

The comfortable world of José and Catalina was about to fall apart. Political times were shifting drastically and people questioned their trust in the government. Even the loyal military men wondered about the future of New Mexico. The Church and government worked against each other. The disharmony agitated strife and provoked the peaceful ambiance.

Catalina and José sensed it was a season when the status quo demanded severe silence. It was a time for listening.

Summer 1661

San Felipe

Catalina López Romero de Telles Xirón

Fifth Generation

Chapter 14

Sitting on the porch of the *estancia* of her home in San Felipe, Catalina was shaded from the hot late morning June sun. Her small adept hands were working on the *colcha* embroidery her mother had taught her to stitch. Descending from a family of weavers from Toledo, she wove her own cloth and dyed her own handspun *churro* wool for the embroidery thread.

Quick even stitches of natural dark brown *churro* wool filled in the Tree of Life pattern she was creating. This pattern was a design her father had told her that his paternal grandmother had brought from her native Toledo. The soft wool blended into a circle representing the Tree of Life that women made in the Iberian Peninsula and was passed on to subsequent females in the family. Patterns for the designs were shaped and embellished by the artist.

Catalina's gold wedding band sparkled with the rays of sun peeking through the *viga* on the porch. Her oval shaped face was crowned by cascading jet-black curly hair. Her hazel eyes surveyed the uncovered *sabanilla* needing to be embroidered as her artisan mind visualized the shapes and colors of the completed textile. The sun shimmered on the gold and silver of the old damascene brooch while reflecting on the pool of water from last night's rain.

An old Spanish olive jar caught the water from the rooftop draining off the *canal* from the summer rains. Water was precious in the desert. Catalina used the rainwater for the weekly Friday baths and the washing of clothes. It was a soft water that was gentle to the skin. Sometimes she added the *rosa de castilla* petals to perfume the water for cooking purposes or used the petals as a deodorizer.

Two long strands of pearls hung around the neck of her light brown skin. The pearls glistened like ivory against the thick brown adobe bricks of the house. Her father had a pearl bracelet fashioned with a chunk of red coral embedded in fine silver made for her as a gift for her twelfth birthday. Because Catalina was such a beautiful girl, he wanted her to wear the coral to protect her from the malicious jealousy of other people giving her the *mal de ojo*, the evil jealous curse of persons wanting to casting a spell on her with a single glance of envy.

Catalina fastened her damascene pin to the high neck of her blouse. The pearls, coral and damascene brooch represented a jeweler's mosaic of Jewish, Arab and Christian periods of Spain. These influences were transported to the dry desert of the far away province of New Mexico. Like a portrait of a Spanish beauty dressed in a white fine linen blouse and black silk skirt adorned with Iberian jewels, Catalina was framed by the New Mexico majestic lapis mountains coalescing in the variegated salmon pink mesa desert.

In the distance near the enveloping mesa, a chocolate brown stallion pounded its hooves on the soft beige sand. The confident rider was an experienced horseman, ready for action on the vast space of unknown surprises and perils of this enchanted land.

Recognizing the silhouette against the bright turquoise sky nearing the *encomienda*, Catalina ran to embrace the man, "*Papacito*, how are you, my father?" she said as she ran up to hug him.

"*Mi hija*, I am so happy to see you, my precious daughter," roared this fit middle-aged man with a commanding presence.

"*Pase, pase*. Come into the house and sit down. Let me bring you some fresh water from the *noria*. Well water is the best and it will cool your parched throat on this dry day. Hopefully, we will have another afternoon rain to cool off the hot days here," she said.

Pouring a cup of fresh water into the handmade ceramic cup, Catalina handed the gold tinged clay vessel to her father. Bartolomé Romero III emptied the liquid in one gulp. She gave him another cup and this time he sipped the water slowly.

Admiring the tiles near the adobe corner fireplace, the father commented on the decor saying, "These are the blue bird tiles your husband brought from Puebla. What memories they stir up inside me. Until now, I had forgotten that my father used to tell me that his grandmother once owned this Chinese teapot she brought with her from Spain. Your pattern reminds me of the blueness of the pottery. Your uncle, Matías Romero, broke this pot one fall morning when he was reaching for a bowl of freshly roasted pine nuts. *Ay, Dio*, was he ever in trouble. Enough of these stories! How are you doing today?" he asked her.

"*Papacito*, why do you say "*Dio*" instead of "*Dios*" when you speak?" inquired his daughter.

"This is an excellent question, my daughter. I say this because we worship one G-d, not multiple gods. *Conversos* believe this word is core to our belief system," answered Bartolomé.

"*Gracias, Papacito*, for explaining the reason. I am doing fine, thanks to the graciousness of our ever present *Eterno*. To be truthful, I am worried about my husband. This governor, Bernardo López de Mendizábal, is such a hard and unrelenting man. I feel the strain he causes in our own home. How are you, *Papacito?*" she probed as her evergreen eyes bore through the layers of formality and centered on an honest response.

Looking down at the brown and gray *jerga* cloth covering the kitchen area, he hesitated and said, "Governor López is a most difficult man to please. He is not content with anything that we do here. *Don* Bernardo rules as a governor filled with a kingdom of demons inside him," stated the father. "I am afraid that his harshness will cause turmoil and hardship on all of us, my precious. Now that I am mayor of Santa Fe, I understand the depth of his depravity," he added.

Fixating his eyes on an object draped on the wooden chest with Moorish geometric rosettes, he said, "Oh, my, you are making a *colcha* quite similar to the one Catalina from Toledo made. Luisa Robledo de Romero put it away in such a safe place that it is still lost. My daughter, when you were born, I had to name you after her. You had her green eyes and somehow your strong independent spirit reminds me of her. I cannot believe that you are making a replica of the same pattern she used. Did you ever see her work?" he asked.

"No, father, I heard about it and this is what I saw in my head. I believe that the Tree of Life springs from inside my heart. I know this sounds strange, but many times I feel like I know Catalina López from Toledo. I know things that I have not been taught. Then there are times that I sense that the Romeros from Corral del Almaguer braid spiritual knowledge with Grandmother Catalina deep inside my soul," disclosed Catalina to her father.

Deep *arroyos* of quietness filled the moment. Brushing his hair away from his forehead with his hand, the startled father said, "You are the daughter of my maternal and paternal families. You see Catalina, it is whispered in the family that we descend from *marranos,* also known as Jewish families, from Spain. I personally do not like this word although the people here use it to refer to persons of Jewish blood. I prefer to use the word *converso* because we were forced to become Christians."

Pausing to phrase his thoughts precisely, he continued, "You do not know this, but I often observe your Jewishness in your thinking. I know how I raised you. For example, how did you know to use the *colcha* pattern you chose for the Tree of Life? It is in your blood and in your soul, my daughter. *Está en la sangre.* You have to understand that we left Spain to seek a life away from the power of the Inquisition. As for me, I have to pretend to be Catholic. But in my heart, I know that I am of *converso* spirit. This is precisely why I am so disturbed by the actions of *Don* Bernardo. They say he is a Jew. His actions remind me of Torquemada—hard on his own people. Torquemada was a Jew in Spain who became a Christian and then became an official of the Inquisition. Be careful, I sense something bad may happen, this is why I came to see you today."

Catalina sighed softly. Now she finally understood why she was not happy with the church. At last, her father's echoing words voiced why she felt so different. He taught her to say the Spanish prayer for lighting candles. Yet, this was the first time daughter and father really talked about the meaning of belonging to a crypto-Jewish family.

The grandfather took his grandchildren to the *portal* and gave them some *piñon* nuts he picked himself. Rafael begged his grandfather to please sing a song before he left. Yielding to the collective request of his grandchildren, the *abuelo* sang *Don Gato:*

"*Estaba el gatito prieto en su silleta sentad
con su media de pelillo y zapato alpargatado.
Le han llegado las noticias que había de ser casado
con una gata morita hija del gato bragado.
El gato de la alegría se cayó de arriba abajo
se ha quebrado la cabeza y la mitad del espinazo.
Tráiganle quien le confiese al gatito enamorado.
Confieso a mi confesor que he sido un gato malvado.*

Y si de ésta no me escapo no me entierren en sagrado
entiérrenme en un arroyo donde me pise el ganado
que digan los gachupines "Aquí murió el malhadado
no murió de tabardillo ni de dolor de costado
murió de un dolor de amores que le dio desesperado."
Los ratones que lo saben se visten de colorado
a lo español y francés lo que le luce al soldado."

The children squealed and laughed to hear of the cat in love. After visiting briefly with his grandchildren, Bartolomé III hugged his daughter with a hug extending from his fingertips stretching from the tormenting times of 1391 Sevilla to the grueling time of 1661 in New Mexico. He mounted his horse and galloped over the celery colored yucca dotted mesas leading back to the *villa* of Santa Fe. It would take him the rest of the afternoon of hard riding to make it home for a light supper with his wife, Josefa Archuleta.

After putting the children to bed early that evening, Catalina went out to the porch and watched the apricot moon hang on the breast of the robin egg sky. Feeling lonely, she had hoped that José would come home today. As the last rays of light melded into a velvety indigo sky, Catalina knew that her husband would not make it home tonight either. José appeared to be under relentless stress lately. Governor López had been making some rigorous demands on him and everyone else in the province.

Only twenty-one years old and the mother of three sons and one daughter, Catalina had a deep love for her husband. She first saw José Telles Xirón in Santa Fe in 1654 when she was fourteen-years old. In her mind, she saw him as she first saw him...almost six feet tall, of muscular stature and with white skin surrounded by a head full of ebony wavy hair. His black mustache added maturity and an air of elegance to his youth. His coffee brown eyes locked into her sage green eyes and magic happened. Within only three months, this handsome soldier married the daughter of the well-known Romero family.

José was a native of Los Altos de San Jacinto de Coyoacán, near Mexico City. He told her that his family settled in Mexico City in 1529. The first Telles father, a lawyer, defended Indians before the Inquisition. This patriarch had eighteen children and died a poor man. All of the children had to scramble to earn their fortunes. As a young man seeking fortune and a good life, José was eager to leave Coyoacán and make a new life in the province of New Mexico. Consequently, he joined the military and was willing to risk his life in the lonely wilderness of New Mexico. Little did he know that his fortune would include marrying the lovely Catalina, the jewel of his modest life.

Catalina thought about the delicate hand painted blue and white bird tiles her husband bought for her from Puebla. He purchased them at the market in Mexico City as a birthday present for his wife. For her last birthday, he purchased some long gold filigree seed pearl earrings. José told Catalina he thought of her as his pearl because she was priceless to him. Her heart grew warm merely thinking about him.

José Telles owned the *encomiendas* of San Felipe and Cochiti. His family lived a comfortable life. Yet, intuitively, Catalina knew something was going to happen. As she gazed in to the midnight blue night, a pack of coyotes serenaded the almond milk moon arching in the sky. Suddenly, hundreds of falling stars fell abruptly from the heavens leaving sapphire and citrine trails and then evaporated into a fathomless tangible dark infinity.

Summer turned into autumn. The pumpkin moon glowed with ripening vines of the productive agricultural harvest. Wheat, pine nuts, beans, hides, corn, *habas, calabazas* and chile were plentiful. This was the season to dry vegetables, fruit and meat for the cold, long winter months. Finally, it seemed that the winter food was stored in the barn or the *soterrano,* an underground place for storing vegetables and fruit. Strong odors of freshly harvested food drifted across the rich terrain of the abundant Río Grande Valley smelling like a rich perfume.

Catalina was occupied with the task of storing food for her family. With four small children, one of them always needed a hug or attention. She felt glad that her days on the *estancia* were demanding because José was either in Santa Fe or on some military journey. She worried about him because his happy face had changed to a blank pensive look. Rumors were circulating about *Don* Bernardo being cruel to the Indians, not promoting Christianity among Indians, not repairing the local prison, accepting bribes, abusing his authority with women and oppressing ecclesiastics. At the same time, the people were afraid of him because he had the power to take away lands and have them flogged or worse.

Despite the wretched fear invading the province, José had to do something special for his Catalina. From Governor López's store, he purchased moss green velvet fabric for a new dress. He also purchased raspberry silk material for petticoats and a matching blouse. He wanted his Catalina to dress in Europe's finest textiles. Having his wife dress in quality fabric made him feel rich because it made him feel good to give such a gift.

After the fabrics were made into clothes, José caught his breath to see how lovely Catalina looked in the new outfit. The colors were perfect and refreshing to the eye. He loved his wife deeper than the bottomless canyons near Taos.

In the plentiful cornucopia of autumn, a shadow loomed over the Telles household. Despite the glowing harvest moon, little light permeated on the Telles Xirón *encomienda.* It was a season of spiritual drought darkened by almost no light.

Autumn, 1661

San Felipe

Catalina López Romero de Telles Xirón

Fifth Generation

Chapter 15

T he clean Santa Fe air sparked with apprehension. Wind puffs of distrust and questions of loyalty were rampant on the dusty plaza. In this City of Holy Faith, mere survival was the essence of life. In the summer of 1643, eight of New Mexico's best native sons had been beheaded for "sedition" regarding the murder of ex-governor Luis Rosas. If the sons of the *conquistadores* were admonished with such cavalier disregard, what was the future inheritance of the grandsons and granddaughters of these Spanish leaders? What had happened to the titles of *nobleza?*

Governor *Don* Bernardo López de Mendizábal created another decade of anxiety in the province of New Mexico. The governor's treatment of Indians, women, clergy as well as of the colonists was harsh. He was rumored to have falsified reports and engaged in creating financial opportunities for him at the expense of human dignity. His trusted local officials included Diego Romero, Nicolás de Aguilar, Cristóbal Anaya Almazán and Francisco Gómez Robledo.

Don Bernardo had the support of his wife, *Doña* Teresa de Aguilera; they were a tight spousal team. No one knew why this couple was exiled to desolate New Mexico. Servants spoke of the couple as being Jews and living in a place they did not like. Hearsay focused on the couple changing their clothes on Friday and taking Friday night baths.

Catalina worried about her family. She remembered seeing the stars fall from the heavens the previous summer. Still, nothing had happened. Living in San Felipe, she would visit with her parents every other month. Mayor Romero, as a political figure, was concerned about the welfare of all Santa Fe citizens.

Long discussions in the plaza of Santa Fe buzzed around the recent church announcement. The Church had a spiritual responsibility to guard the flock from heresy and keep unclean persons away from good Christians. Friar Alonso Benavides was appointed as *comisario* in Santa Fe in 1625. Thirty years later, Friar Alonso de Posada served as *comisario* and his duty was to investigate crimes for the Inquisition. In the fall of 1661, the Edict of Faith was read in church. Formal Inquisition proclamations were read to citizens to remind Catholics of church doctrine. Catalina and her parents discussed the implications of the Holy Catholic Church addressing the issue of Jewish practices in this document. The mandatory decree by the "Inquisitors of the Archbishopric of Mexico" was read to all persons at church services. Another formal reading to describe the practices of *conversos* only meant that there was suspicion of crypto-Jews practicing Judaism in New Mexico.

Inquisitors were to visit each town once a year and the *comisario* gathered evidence for the Holy Church. The Saturday before the reading of the Edict of Faith, a proclamation was made requiring each person in the community to attend Mass or face excommunication. After church members heard the detailed descriptions of the Edict of Faith, alleged heretics were to be reported to the *comisario* within the period of six days. Neighbors and relatives were to inform an agent about any suspicious activities or possible heretics. Edicts were printed and nailed on the church doors.

Friar Posada had given Mayor Romero a personal copy of the *Edicto de Fe*. With a heavy spirit, the mayor folded up the proclamation to share later in the day with his family. After eating dinner, the mayor opened the announcement and in a slow deliberate voice, Bartolomé read the Edict of Faith to his family. When he completed reading the edict aloud, he said, "This is a most grave situation. We have to be extremely cautious about displaying absolute loyalty to the Church. We can never forget our family left Spain hiding from the Inquisition. May *El Eterno* remember us in our terrifying trial." He placed his hand on Catalina and prayed for a blessing for his daughter.

After discussing the ramifications of the *Edicto de Fe* with her parents, Catalina calculated the high degree of fear she saw in her father's eyes. When she went to bed the following evening, she tossed and turned. Finally going to sleep, she dreamed of being in a large dark room and smelled a putrefied stench penetrating the air. Catalina recognized a young grandmother hiding a beige silk altar cloth under her long dark blue skirt. Dim outlines of a tree with eagles decorated the textile. On one visible corner of the cloth, dark crimson pomegranates concealed red droplets.

An older woman, perhaps the mother of the woman with the fabric, braced her fragile body against the younger woman's hip. The two women stood in front of a twenty-foot sturdy hand carved oak table. Two well-dressed erudite Catholic officials were seated on ornately impressed oak and burgundy leather chairs. Another middle-aged man, a notary, with his back hunched over piles of papers, recorded the session.

One large cream colored vase broke the darkness of the atmosphere. The only blue decoration on the container was an ominous hand painted large crest crowned with a royal coronet. Inside the shield of the crest, were the symbols of an olive branch, cross and sword. The obscure code of the urn was clear...the Spanish Crown and Holy Catholic Cross were married to bring justice with the sword by extending an olive branch of mercy to the heretic living on Spanish soil. If the accused person pledged total faith to the Church by the authority of the Holy Office of the Inquisition, then mercy on the heretic resulted in Spanish citizenship. Otherwise, the heretic would be punished with a sharpened sword.

In the stillness of the hearing room, the stale air crackled with a boom. Looking at the trembling middle age woman, the Inquisitor said to the younger woman, "So you do admit to washing off the Sacrament of Baptism of your grandchildren. This is a most serious offense and several witnesses have testified how you washed off the holy oil and water while praying for a guardian angel."

Turning his attention to the older woman, the small eyes of the refined man focused on her as she braced herself with both hands on the rough edge of the table, he laid out the accusations,

Your friends and family testified that you violated our faith in many ways. By the standards of the Edict of Faith, you displayed the following transgressions:

- *Observing the Sabbath;*
- *Wearing clean clothes on Friday;*
- *Eating kosher food;*
- *Fasting on Jewish holidays;*
- *Burning hair and finger/toe nail clippings;*
- *Washing hands before praying;*
- *Celebrating Passover;*
- *Observing Sucott, known as cabañuelas;*
- *Observing Hanuka;*
- *Drinking Kosher wine;*
- *Circumcising children;*
- *Washing off baptismal oil and water of newborn babies;*
- *Having guardian angels or hadas for newborn babies;*
- *Burning a piece of masa as a sacrifice;*
- *Washing a corpse with warm water;*

- *Placing a pearl or virgin soil on the corpse;*
- *Throwing out water in the home of the deceased; and*
- *Saying the Law is as good as the Law of Jesus Christ.*

Raising his voice, he added, "Tomorrow is Sunday and it the day of the auto de fe. It is your Judgment Day. You were raised in a family belonging to Santa María La Blanca Sinagoga and lived in the judería. You will appear in the auto de fe and will be burned to death as a religious criminal. Seven years ago you confessed to being "reconciled" with the Church and have relapsed by adhering to the said Jewish practices."

Catalina then saw the two women walking down the cobblestone streets in a long procession. The old woman wore a coarse cotton gray *samarra* vest painted with torches and devils. The younger woman wore a yellow linen *sambenito* with a red cross. Both women wore long pointed hats and walked on a stage where hundreds of persons were gathered below to watch the ceremony.

A Mass was said by the dignitaries and the altar was draped in black cloth. The younger woman was called up on stage and "reconciliation" required her to wear the *sambenito* for three years. When last name of the criminals was called, the lone *viejita* limped to the front of the stage and was told that because of her heresy that she was sentenced to be burned.

The old woman hobbled to the pyre where she was tied to the stake. With no hesitation, an ambitious political merchant, recently made wealthy by purchasing fabrics from a Jew being investigated by the Inquisition, lit the pyre. As the hot flames were engulfing the woman at the *quemadero*, in a voice that petrified the large crowd, she yelled clearly in a steady voice, "*El Eterno es Dio de Ysrael.*"

Catalina awoke from the frenzied sleep. Sitting up in bed, she rubbed her eyes because the dream was quite real.

Somehow, these women from this *plaza* on a hill were familiar to her. Catalina held on tightly to the border of her pillow. As she went back to sleep again, her hand clenched the pillow having the exact embroidered pomegranate design of the altar cloth of her dream.

This time Catalina dreamed of sitting under an olive tree and wept for the unsung forgotten melodies of her family. The two grandmothers, dressed in their *sambenitos*, prayed over Shabbat candles thanking Hashem that Catalina was a Toledo tradition keeper.

When she awoke the following morning, Catalina realized this Edict of Faith proclamation was the basis of the *comisario* gathering evidence from others to initiate inquisitorial proceedings. She was thankful that she lived in San Felipe and not in Santa Fe or Toledo. From this day forward, Catalina would be more vigilant about her actions in the privacy of her own home. She would observe the Sabbath, light Friday night candles, wash off the baptism oils and water, believe in *hadas*, cook the first *tortilla* and throw it away and place a pearl in the mouth of dead loved one. Catalina was worried and had to think of a plan to hide from others. She did not want to be reported to the *comisario* for heresy.

She heard from others that her cousin, Diego Romero, was a strong supporter of the governor. Another cousin, the son of Ana Robledo, Francisco Gómez Robledo, was also supportive of the governor. She feared for the safety of her two cousins.

Catalina was resting on a leather chair on the *portal* enjoying the November evening. The children were playing and laughing with each other. As evening dressed into night, the lonely call of the coyote chilled the warm cholla cacti churning in the sandy soil. The coyote was howling a destitute doleful dirge in the desert land. Catalina felt a twinge in her heart and listened to the coyote crying.

The following afternoon, the children were playing together inside the house. Children loved to play even when things in their world were not going well. Grandfather Bartolomé taught them to play *Ángel Bueno* and *Ángel Malo*. Grandfather told the children that on *Shabbat* that each person had the choice of selecting the good or the bad angel to pursue on *sábado*. Then the children followed the rules of the game. Two of the siblings were chosen to represent the two angels and a color was assigned. The other two siblings were placed on opposite sides. After guessing the correct color, the children held hands pulling in opposite directions to see which side won.

Rafael started the game by saying:

"Voy quebrando
Bolitas de oro. Tan, tan.
¿Quién es?
El Ángel Malo.
¿Qué quiere el Ángel Malo?
Colores.
¿Qué color?"[ii]

As the children were ready to choose a color for the game, someone pounding on the door startled the occupants and interrupted the game. Important military officials stood in the doorway of the Telles Xirón home. The officials informed José that he was being escorted to jail for not following the mandates of Governor Bernardo López de Mendizábal. Brave as ever, José displayed no emotion as the charges by Governor López de Mendizábal were read to him. The soldiers were taking José to the public jail in Taos, over one hundred and twenty miles north, because of his refusal to make statements in a report the governor had requested of him. The notice stated:

Within my rights, I will express documentation to Joseph Telles stating that I am taking away his two encomiendas...he is a young man without sense...and that he not speak about this encomienda or others like it; destiny like those taken away for the past sedition and death of General Don Luis de Rosas for which the grandfather of the wife of Joseph Telles was executed.[e]

As José was taken away by horseback to Taos, all he could see thorough his bleary tired eyes were his three sons, daughter and his wife, Catalina, all hugging each other on the *portal.* When would he return? He could not and would not falsify the report that Governor López de Mendizábal wanted him to sign. His honor was core to his personal integrity.

How could this leader make Catalina relive the death of her grandfather, Juan de Archuleta, beheaded for the murder of Luis Rosas? A total of eight men, including Juan de Archuleta, were beheaded on the plaza. What type of a man would degrade a woman having nothing to do with a past murder? What deception grew in the heart of this official? This was another prime example of how the governor treated women in New Mexico.

While incarcerated in the Taos jail, José became melancholy being separated from his home and family. As he rationalized the basis for the accusation against him, he realized he needed to respond formally to the charges. He wrote the following rebuttal to *Don* Bernardo:

"Besides this, you have in your power my papers of title and services my encomienda so at the end it appears that this is my justice and I am not afraid of what you do with your natural perverseness and outrageous work, which have done overall by using roguery and tyranny. I began to surmise that my children, while I am in exile, were even able to eat, as though these were not the lands of the *Rey Señor.* And this is the sign of the cross that my petition is true and without malice with only wanting to reach ultimate justice."ᵗ

An honest man of upright character, José was not going to be intimidated by a devious governor. He worried in his cell about providing food for his children and wife. Would the King allow his subjects to be treated without any justice?

New Mexicans, in the middle of physical and spiritual droughts, discussed the incarceration of José Telles Xirón. Idle talk centered on the caliber of governors sent to New Mexico as being substandard. How could *Don* Bernardo justify himself in implicating Catalina for something her grandfather did long ago? Old reputable citizens claimed Rosas was another Spanish governmental opportunist trying to make money for a short stint in the province. Higher echelon officials serving in New Mexico were interested in doing well on the job to advance to a higher administrative position in a more prestigious place.

Luis Rosas was allegedly involved romantically with the beautiful wife of one of his own soldiers. Rosas pursued the young wife of the soldier while the husband was away in Mexico City on official business. María Pérez de Bustillo, the wife of the soldier, was admired as a woman of beauty that equaled the courts of Spain. Her mother, Juana Zamora, daughter of Cristóbal Baca and Ana Ortiz, was said to have had fine porcelain facial features.

María Pérez de Bustillo's family came to her rescue for the dishonor Rosas brought on the family and they killed him. Eight men were convicted for his death and beheaded. The five relatives were: Juan Archuleta, Antonio Baca, Nicolás Pérez de Bustillo, Diego Marqués and Juan Ruíz de Hinojas. The other three men, Cristóbal Enriquez, Diego Martin Barba and Francisco de Salazar appeared to have had other motives.

Did the King of Spain endorse such weak leaders such as Rosas and López to lead the citizens of New Mexico? New Mexicans were the sons and daughters of the *conquistadores* and the *madres* of strong colonial stock. Would this same situation happen in Spain?

Catalina cried for her grandfather, Juan Archuleta. This grandfather had the reputation of being an outstanding citizen. He left his name on Inscription Rock in 1632 and 1636. He was the son of a *conquistador*. At the trial, they took away his *encomienda*. Now Governor López listed her name against her husband. Why? What would happen to her children? Why did the women in her family have such difficult lives?

Subsequently, Catalina studied her Tree of Life *colcha* and felt the strength of the textile art. Yes, she had faced many adverse trials in her life. Life truly was like the woolen tree of her fabric design. Some years, the rings were full when nourishment was plentiful. Other years, the rings had thin bands reflecting marginal bare survival. The fact that the tree was able to survive in good and bad times was a major accomplishment in itself.

A flashback of hundreds of falling stars with streaming rainbow ribbons evaporating in the sky inundated her brain and soul. In the darkness of her apprehension, it was a time for consternation.

1663

Mexico City

The Mexican Inquisition

Chapter 16

A mean moving March dust devil blazed through middle of the plaza in Santa Fe. Little rain and less snow had moistened the dry earth begging for water. The drought drained the drying high desert. News from Mexico City drifted in slowly about the New Mexicans appearing before the Inquisitors. Since the Edict of Faith was read in 1661, few citizens readily shared intimate personal information with each other. Each person viewed the other on the streets and at social events with watchful eyes. The mood was prickly. Based on the testimony of unknown witnesses, six persons were now being tried for heresy. Formal charges could be filed against anyone demonstrating an action contrary to the interpretation of the Holy Mother Church. Another dust devil of fear whirred in the colony of New Mexico.

Fray Alonso de Posada, *comisario* of the Inquisition in New Mexico, conducted various interviews in the early 1660's. Resulting from his investigations, six New Mexicans were charged of heresy.

In 1662, former Governor Bernal López de Mendizábal and his wife, *Doña* Teresa de Aguilera, were accused of practicing Jewish traditions. Four New Mexico soldiers were placed under the rigorous scrutiny of the Holy Office. The soldiers, strong supporters of *Don* Bernardo, were charged with heresy and other solemn offences. Diego Romero, Nicolás de Aguilar, Cristóbal de Anaya Almazán and Francisco Gómez Robledo, like *Don* Bernardo and *Doña* Teresa, all awaited their respective trials. In the remote land of New Mexico, the Holy Office of the Inquisition extended its powerful supremacy.

The formal hearing of López began on April 28, 1663 with the tribunal. He was charged for being a descendant of a Jew on the maternal family line. He became ill and due to his failing health, it was evident that this physical factor might impede the Inquisition process. López was charged with accusations that ranged from his alleged involvement of denial of ecclesiastical authority and jurisdiction, poor treatment of the friars, Indian labor, laxity in fulfilling Christian responsibilities, practicing Jewish customs, displaying a negative attitude toward the Holy Office and testifying to the tribunal that none of his ancestors had been tried and found guilty of practicing Judaism.

The tribunal discovered that *Don* Bernardo did not tell the truth about his ancestors not having been arrested or tried by the Inquisition. His mother's grandfather, Juan Núñez de León, was found guilty in 1603 for practicing Judaism.

In three and one half months, many hearings were needed to record *Don* Bernardo's accounts. An attorney was appointed to help him with his case. His physical health continued to decline and the stress of the hearings caused him to tire more easily. In June, he requested that he be moved to a cell having access to ventilation.

Before the Inquisitors reached a decision regarding his guilt, *Don* Bernardo died on September 16, 1664. He was buried in unconsecrated ground near a secret prison of the Holy Office. On April 30, 1671, the tribunal absolved the memory of *Don* Bernardo López de Mendizábal. On May 12, 1671, his bones were exhumed and placed in the chapel of the church of Santo Domingo in Mexico City.

Doña Teresa de Aguilera y Roche was tried concurrently with her husband. During her numerous hearings before the tribunal, *Doña* Teresa shared many stories of misconduct by the friars and the ex-governor, Juan Manso.

Her servants accused her of practicing Jewish customs. The servants had observed her and her husband bathing and washing hair on Friday, changing linens on Friday, taking special care to celebrate on Saturday by primping and not attending Good Friday services.

Her servants accused her of reading books in foreign languages. These same servants believed that the books probably contained heresy.

Doña Teresa's defense was that the witnesses were jealous of her and were motivated by malice. She described her servants as constantly causing trouble. She admitted to being angry with her husband for not warning her that Jews bathed on Friday. On December 19, 1664, the tribune suspended the case against her.

Living in poverty, *Doña* Teresa petitioned the tribunal for a share of the embargoed property she and her husband had owned. In the final disposition of the property, the Inquisitors ordered the sale of the joint property in 1678 with proceeds allocated to the agent of the Holy Office.

Other New Mexicans tried for heresy included Diego Romero. Born in New Mexico, his mother was María Romero, daughter of Bartolomé Romero. His father was Gaspar Pérez, soldier of the Spanish Netherlands. He had no formal education and was a close associate of *Don* Bernardo. On September 19, 1663, the tribunal considered the accusations against Diego after investigating information that he had stated that priests had no spiritual relationships with a baptized infant or the parents and this was in conflict with church doctrine. Diego was accused of displaying a profound hatred toward the friars.

Romero stated that his information about the priest and baptismal relationships with child and parents was based upon a book he had read. However, he told the Inquisitors that he could not read. He gave abundant information about the other soldiers.

During January of 1664, the Inquisitors voted and found Diego guilty. On October 31, 1664, at the preliminary sentence, Diego was labeled an "apostate heretic." Romero would participate in a public *auto de fe* and abjure his errors. He was condemned to serve in the Philippine galleys for four years. He was not to wear gold, silver, pearls, silk or carry arms or ride a horse.

Diego petitioned the court to reconsider his case. The tribunal reconsidered the case and on December 7, 1664, Diego was banished from New Mexico for ten years and was to take up residence in Parral.

Nicolás de Aguilar's trial started on May 8, 1663. He was a native of Michoacán and was married to Catalina Márques, a New Mexico native. Aguilar was accused of infringing on ecclesiastical jurisdiction and immunity, prohibiting the service of Indians at the churches and demonstrating hostile conduct toward the friars and the Church. The friars referred to him as "Atilla" because he was stubborn and direct. Aguilar testified that he allowed these Indian practices to take place because he was following the instructions of his superior officer, Governor López. His heresy was not related to Judaism.

During January of 1664, he pleaded to the tribunal that the facts of his case stemmed from his following the order of his civil superior. The Inquisitors considered his argument and he was finally sentenced on November 23, 1664. Aguilar was banished from New Mexico for ten years and was ineligible to serve in an administrative office and had to appear in a public *auto de fe*. He made his public *auto de fe* in the convent of Santo Domingo. Aguilar abjured his errors on December 17 and was once again a free man.

Cristóbal de Anaya Almazán first appeared before the Inquisitors on April 26, 1663. He was the son of Francisco de Anaya, a citizen of the province of New Mexico. His mother was Juana López de Villafuerte. Almazán was charged with heresy by denying the priest's role in baptizing infants. He testified that his comments were made on the basis of the misconduct he had observed of certain friars in New Mexico. Later, he admitted his guilt of stating to others that priests did not contract spiritual relationship with baptized children and their parents.

During December 1664, Anaya was ordered to appear in a public *auto de fe* and appear at a local church and publicly recant his false teachings. He made his abjuration and on Sunday, July 19, 1665, Anaya appeared in the church of Sandia and confessed his heresy.

Francisco Gómez Robledo was the fourth solider tried before the tribunal in Mexico City. His father was Francisco Gómez, the son of Manuel Gómez and Ana Vicente of Coina, Portugal. His mother was Ana Robledo, daughter of Bartolomé Romero and Luisa Robledo.

His hearing started on May 16, 1663. Francisco was accused of denying the priest relationship with baptized child and family, coming from a family of Jews and harboring hatred and lack of respect for the Holy Mother Church.

However, there were suspicions that Francisco was Jewish because he was circumcised. He explained that he suffered from ulcers. Physicians reported that the scars on his body could have been caused by illness. Francisco testified that there was no proof that his father was a Jew because his father was a Christian in good standing.

As for demonstrating hatred for the Church, Francisco discounted this accusation. He stated that his home was always open to the friars. His fluency in Indian languages aided the priests in their mission work. He testified that he tried to be constructive in edifying the Church mission services. He stated that his grandmother, Catalina López de Robledo, returned to Spain after living in New Mexico. On October 23, 1664, the Inquisitors rendered their sentence. They voted to acquit Francisco of all charges and adjusted the costs of the trial.

Don Bernardo López died in prison and lost all of his material wealth. Before dying, he admitted that his mother's father was tried by the Inquisition for practicing Judaism. His wife blamed him for allowing her to bathe, change linens and observe Jewish traditions. *Doña* Teresa de Aguilera was left penniless after her long incarceration and loss of her husband.

Aguilar, not a New Mexico native, was banished from New Mexico for ten years. Anaya, Romero and Gómez were natives of New Mexico. All three soldiers were supporters of Governor López. Anaya confessed his heresy. Since Romero had committed the most serious heresy, he was banished from New Mexico for ten years.

Gómez was acquitted of all charges, specifically for suspicion of being a Jew. Although Francisco rendered this testimony about his grandmother, Catalina López de Robledo, returning to Spain, was he telling the truth? Being tried for heresy, he wanted to save himself from being found guilty. This was a life or death charge against him. Would a mother and grandmother leave all of her children to return to a far away country not honoring her religious beliefs? Catalina López was unable to defend herself at the trial of her grandson. In reality, there was no documentation to prove that the grandmother returned to Spain. According to the tribunal, there was no supporting evidence to substantiate Jewish charges against Francisco Gómez.

In the end, after all the hearings and verdicts, the Inquisitors did not address the common blood yoke between Diego Romero and Francisco Gómez. Both cousins knew of the crypto-Jewish custom of washing off the baptismal sacrament of the baby. Perhaps the volume of paperwork in the Spanish Empire inhibited the officials from gleaning updated family history. Or perhaps the *conversos* were shrewd in hiding their true identities. These two New Mexican soldiers were mere Jewish cousins living in an unwelcome frontier surviving the Inquisition. Like their ancestors in La Mancha, the cousins were living the impossible dream of worshipping like Jews and fighting the windmills of the Mexican Inquisition. Like their ancestors in Castilla, they were religious hostages in isolated lands.

Outside of New Mexico within the same time period, other persons in Mexico accused of being Jews were not so fortunate relative to the final verdicts of the tribunal. Ana Gómez, of Tacubaya, was burned in 1649. Her husband, Diego Díaz, eighty years old, was burned alive in 1659. In 1667, Baltazar Pereyra, Portuguese, was fined 2,000 pesos to be paid to the Holy Office. In 1688, Diego de Alvarado, known as Muñoz, a resident of Puebla, died in the secret cells. In 1678, Antonio Lorenzo, known as Francisco de Medina, was sent to Manila for being a Jew. In 1696, Pedro Carretero, known as Pedro de la Vega, native of Tlaxcala, received 200 lashes while sentenced to serve six years in the Philippine galleys. Fernando de Medina, resident of Mexico, also known as Alberto Moisés Gómes, was burned alive.

Catalina appeared calm; however, she was mortified to hear the news about crypto-Jews in New Mexico being tried by the Inquisition in Mexico City. Her friends told her that they were traumatized to learn of the heresy of their own New Mexican neighbors. She feigned shock and mostly listened to the conversations of others.

As she made *buñuelos* for *Hanuka*, she prayed for forgiveness for *Don* Bernardo and *Doña* Teresa. The governor and his wife were embroiled in petty politics. Catalina would have preferred sharing the discourse of religious perspectives and learning new Jewish knowledge. Catalina would have relished sharing an intellectual dialog with *Doña* Teresa discussing the books in her library.

She marveled at the cleverness of her cousins, Diego and Francisco, in providing credible logic to the Inquisitors. Everyone in New Mexico knew that crypto-Jews washed off the oil and the water of infant baptism. This practice was specified in the Edict of Faith, which had been read to them many times at church. Diego only verbalized what he knew and he did not have to read a book to comprehend this knowledge. And New Mexicans all knew that Francisco and his brothers had been circumcised. Their grandmother would have been so proud of her grandsons.

She questioned the intelligence of the Inquisitors. How could they not conclude Diego and Francisco were Jews? She was thankful the Inquisitors did not question the motives of *Doña* Ana Robledo and *Doña* Catalina de Zamora being with *Doña* Teresa de Aguilera the night she was arrested for heresy. The Inquisition agents told these women to go home and take their beds with them. These *conversa* women were with *Doña* Teresa to support her.

One point was clear...she would hide even more so now. If she or her relatives were accused of Judaism in the near future, local documents would be studied. She did not want that to happen and ultimately harm friends or relatives. All Catalina could do was to maintain her Jewish practices hoping that *Hashem* would light her path. It was a time for reflection and thanksgiving.

In the province of New Mexico, a harsh dust devil of silence beat the hearts of the *conversos* and their families. There was great fear that a relative or friend would report strange practices to the powerful Inquisitors 2,000 miles away from home. The trials of persons they loved and were related to, ignited panic in their souls. It was a time for shunning friendly embraces. It was a time for stark silence.

1675

Senucú

Catalina López Romero de Telles Xirón

Fifth Generation

Chapter 17

Bright sun yellow roses welcomed the May day. Spring was in the air and another hot sun singed the already balmy May morning. The drought started in 1666 and each year everyone hoped the spring clouds would bring sweet rains to nourish the bodies, minds and dispositions in the colony.

The drought began during the administration of Governor Rosas in 1637. Not only was there an extreme drought, but the governor demanded Indian labor to increase their production of hides, crops and cloth. Luis Rosas had rewarded his political friends with administrative positions and they returned this favor by supporting the governor's wishes. At the conclusion of the Rosas' administration, the Santa Fe community was divided evenly by pro and anti Rosas factions.

Governor Rosas was murdered because of his involvement with María Pérez de Bustillo. Her husband and family contended that Rosas had purposely dishonored the family by using his administrative position to intimidate citizens. Eight of New Mexico's premium soldiers, five men having family ties to María, were beheaded in 1643 on the plaza of Santa Fe. From this date forward, New Mexico citizens displayed acute apprehension in trusting the government. A deep lack of confidence in the government created a chasm in the colony. Citizens feared being reported to the government or the priests. This ambiance of distrust shushed the private talks that normally kindled a unified community. As a direct result of the lack of unity between government and church, Inquisition officials in Mexico City were more involved in New Mexico affairs.

The ongoing drought continued with the administration of Governor Bernardo López de Mendizábal. Like Rosas, López rewarded his cronies and found ways to augment his personal assets.

A spiritual drought was magnified by the six New Mexicans appearing before the Inquisitors of the Mother Church in Mexico City. Trust was decimated within the colony and the citizens did not have confidence in either civil or religious leaders.

"José, do you think white is a pretty color for a dress for our new daughter?" Catalina asked her husband.

"Catalina, *mi querida,* you dress her in any clothing you want to, for any occasion," replied José.

"I want this to be a nice ceremony. I know that in this drought many are suffering from having no food at all. I will serve only hot chocolate and sweets of *empanaditas* stuffed with pumpkin. Hmm, I will make some *bizcochitos* too. My grandmother used her special recipe of butter and homemade chokecherry wine to flavor the dry cookie. All the women want to know the ingredients, but this has been a secret recipe in the family for years and I do not want to give the recipe to just anyone," Catalina told her husband.

Toying with the lukewarm mint tea in his green and white mug from Puebla, he answered, "Do what you desire and enjoy the good times we have now. We suffered enough when Governor López placed me in the Taos jail. I do not want to live those difficult days of my life again. I like living here in Senucú with you, away from everyone."

"I know my husband, but I do miss my family," responded Catalina as her small hand played with the dark hair now having many silver strands reflecting the personal and political pressures she had suffered. "It was better not to go back to Santa Fe after all your trials and the Inquisition trials of my cousins. We have lived in Senucú since 1667 and I know the move was difficult for you. I appreciate your support and love."

"The situation is not good right now. The Indians do not have enough food to eat with the drought. I do not like being unkind to anyone. I have told you many times that my grandfather was a lawyer in Mexico City and represented Indians accused of idolatry by the Inquisition. I hope I am wrong, but with this continued drought, and the Indians not having enough to eat, a solution has to be reached to feed all of us. Many Indians are dying and starving. Please just make one pastry because we need to conserve our food supply. Is this fine with you?" he asked his wife.

"You are so wise and I appreciate your wisdom. Yes, I will only make the *bizochitos* to serve. Our wheat crops are very small and we have just enough to splurge on a treat for our daughter," replied Catalina.

Pouring more hot water into José's mug, Catalina added, "It really could be worse, *mi querido*. What truly amazes me is that the Inquisitors never pieced together that Diego Romero and Francisco Gómez Robledo were cousins. Francisco was acquitted for not being a Jew and Diego was most direct in voicing his belief that priests did not have the authority to baptize babies. Francisco and Diego were grandsons of Catalina López de Robledo and Bartolomé Romero. I have been told that both families were *conversos*—secret Jews from Spain and Portugal," she said and then paused for a moment.

Continuing with this thought, she added, "I believe it is true because I have observed the practices of some of the Jewish traditions the Church read regarding the 1661 Edict of Faith. I knew we had customs we did not share openly, but when I heard that the Church asked community members to report persons carrying out the practices they specified, I felt scared. I feel a loss in not knowing Hebrew and worshipping in freedom. I understand how the Indians feel about being forced to accept Christianity and speak Spanish. Does this make sense? Why do I have to hide celebrating the birth of my daughter? This is not right," commented Catalina.

Animated by the deep dialog, she continued, "After the baptism at the church, I am going to do like my family has always done—we wash off the priest's water and oil from our daughter's head. It will be just us because I am afraid that we can be reported to the Church. Then I will be of no help to you or our children," she said.

"*Ay*, Catalina. You are so insightful. We must protect our children from the priests and the government. Be careful," he whispered.

"I will my husband. Here I am, thirty years old and still having your babies. Our daughter has my green eyes and your dark hair. I like the name we are giving her, María Zapata. When I first held her, I sensed she was special. Women in our family with green eyes have some special spiritual knowledge. My only wish is that our children will follow G-d. I tell G-d that even our dreams belong to Him. Our spirits are wilting in the drought of Catholic baptizing waters. Will our children ever be able to worship freely? I know that you are Catholic, but I suspect that you may have the same Sephardic blood in your veins too," she told him.

"Why do you say this?" he wanted to know.

"My grandfather used to say that he heard that the Telles family lived in Amsterdam and some moved to England. Many of the *conversos* moved to Amsterdam during and after the Alhambra Decree," she replied.

Putting his strong arms around her small waist, he rubbed his nose in her hair. "How could I ever go back to Mexico City when I found you? You are *picosa* like the hot chile of the fields. I pray that María Zapata will have the good fortune of having the spirit of the López Romero blood strengthen her and her children," he murmured as he kissed Catalina on her neck.

After the baptismal ceremony, the Telles Xirón family went home for a private celebration. Catalina made hot chocolate and *bizcochitos*. Yellow roses filled the house and this was a day for a *fiesta*. Food was scarce during the drought but this was a special day. The parents, José, Catalina and the children José, Juan Rafael, Isabel, Jacinta and Juan gathered for a private family celebration.

Catalina placed María Zapata in a ceramic basin José purchased in Mexico City. A mother's hand scrubbed off the water and oil the friar had poured on her daughter's head. Poor María's head turned red where her mother scrubbed so hard. The baby cried and the siblings tried to comfort their baby sister. Rafael, already sixteen years of age, patted his sister's petite hands and assured her everything would be fine. She looked at Rafael with exquisite almond shaped cactus colored eyes. His sister was the most beautiful baby he had seen.

Catalina gave the baby the prescribed bath. Wheat and corn grains, along with coins of silver and gold, were placed in the basin. Exuberance for welcoming the baby into the family permeated the ritual. José threw in a pearl belonging to his mother-in-law. Rafael ran outside and returned with a single *rosa de castilla* flower because this was the closest to gold he could find for his little sister.

After washing María, Catalina put her hands on the baby's head and prayed for health, wealth and good fortune. Then she prayed for a guardian angel to watch over María for all the days of her life.

The older children were delighted with their new baby sister. They remembered the last decade when their father had been taken away from them and placed in jail. Now they lived a different life and became aware of the heartaches of life. The

Telles children learned not to trust the religious friars or the civil government. They observed with their own eyes what the governor did to their father. With their precious souls, they saw what the Inquisitors did to their relatives, Diego Romero and Francisco Gómez Robledo. They recognized it was dangerous to live in the colony practicing Jewish traditions.

Spiritual maturity hardened the children's religious perspective. In the short life of the Telles children, they knew in their hearts that it was a time for vigilance.

The Natives were unhappy with their lives. Most of all, they were treated unfairly by the Spaniards. Since Oñate's arrival in 1598, they had been forced to accept a foreign religion and yield to a new government. European illnesses killed a vibrant community because they had no immune systems to counter the unfamiliar illnesses. In 1636, a smallpox epidemic killed 20,000 out of 60,000 Indians. The Natives lost their physical pueblos too. By 1640, only forty-three settlements remained in use compared to the one hundred and fifty active pueblos Oñate encountered.

In 1643, each Indian had to give one cotton blanket and one bushel of corn to their master four times a year. By 1659, Governor Mendizábal observed the Indians living on grass seed while the Spanish colonists were eating bran, barley and herbs. The governor had the Indians harvesting salt and piñon nuts, tanning hides and weaving blankets for him. Governor Mendizábal allowed the Indians to worship their native gods and the friars were indignant with the governor's interference in their mission work.

Governor Juan Francisco Treviño, arriving in New Mexico in 1675, had Indian sorcerers hung. Forty-seven medicine men were arrested, flogged and then sold as slaves for the sin of practicing witchcraft.

In the rightful minds and eyes of the Natives, life was not fair. Indians of all backgrounds began to unite as one and voice their dissatisfaction against the Spanish Empire.

Parallel to the natives dancing their sacred *kachina* dances, descendants of *conversos,* like Catalina, practiced their own traditions in secrecy. Catalina did not know why she did the things she did, she only mirrored what she observed her parents and grandmother practice. The fear of the Inquisition was quite real and Catalina would not risk her children's lives to be left without a mother. At times she felt like the lone coyote wailing to the honey colored moon.

Her children and family kept her occupied. There were always uncompleted cooking and gardening tasks. Laundry had to be washed and the children needed constant attention and supervision. During her spare time, she loved to weave and color the wool with native dyes. She once told José that she remembered weaving wool on a loom in Toledo and taking her articles to the market to be sold. José laughed at her and told her it was impossible for her to remember something she had never done.

Now approaching forty, age was beginning to show on Catalina's face. The desert had dried her skin and fine lines appeared by the eyes and mouth. Her hair was mostly gray but her figure was still supple and youthful. Catalina's big green eyes beamed like mystical green turquoise, beckoning for more and more.

The children enjoyed seeing their mother dress for special events. Catalina would take out her embroidered silk *rebozo* and black *mantilla* out of the heavy wooden chest. Then she would lift the old white box belonging to a grandmother many years ago from the bottom of the chest to display for special occasions. The white box was placed on a table under the *colcha* she had woven depicting the Tree of Life.

Senecú was not as verdant or cool as Santa Fe, but it was away from the vigilant eyes observing every move. Actually, she felt more at peace here because it was closer to La Toma. Situated near the Río Grande, Senucú was south of Socorro and north of *El Paraje de* Fray Cristóbal and Robledo.

In spring and fall, Catalina and her daughters would visit the Río Grande to watch the migrating birds. Birds of all shapes and sizes swooped down from the pale coral sky to drink the fresh water of the great river. For some unknown reason, she was attracted to birds. Warblers, wrens, cranes and geese would eat right out of her hand. The girls would try to mimic Catalina's movements to attract the birds but the feathered animals kept their distance. However, birds flocked to María Zapata just the way they did to Catalina. María's sisters marveled at their youngest sister's ability to communicate with the birds.

The daughters noticed shortly after María Zapata was born, that a pair of golden eagles frequented their favorite spots. The golden eagles never came near anyone. They simply perched on the highest branches of the regal cottonwood trees watching the Telles females.

Catalina and María Zapata shared an unspoken bond with one another. María's eyes were a lighter hue of green than Catalina's eyes. Most of the time, the two females did not have to speak to each other because they were thinking the same thing. It was an unusual mother daughter relationship and the other sisters recognized the uniqueness of their communication. They exchanged messages with each other with only a glance and not verbalizing any words.

The sons of Catalina were young men and now ready to seek their own fortunes in life. She felt blessed. She loved her husband, sons, daughters and her G-d. As a young girl, her father and mother instructed her to worship on Saturday and follow the Ten Commandments. They told her to add these two items to her Communion lessons but not to tell the priest. Catalina did follow her parents' advice.

There appeared to be a false air of peace in Senucú. Along the banks of the upper and lower Río Grande, vultures basked in the shadows. It was a season of intense peril.

1680

Guadalupe del Paso del Norte
Catalina López Romero de Telles Xirón

Fifth Generation

Chapter 18

O ne quiet February morning gave birth to another warm day. A flock of robins, wintering in the trees of the Río Grande for winter, foraged the soil for food. The last patch of snow melted into rivulets of water edging down the riverbank uncovering a breakfast of burrowing insects for the hungry birds.

Catalina was readying the house for spring-cleaning. It was time to dust the walls and clean the house. In the corner of the adobe home, she was cooking *haba* beans and onions with dried green chile for a hearty meal. The *fogón* emitted enough heat to take the cold out of the early morning. In a big bowl, *masa* was rising for the whole wheat *tortillas* she would cook on the *comal* to eat with the Friday stew.

In the light of the window covered with mica to filter sunlight into the house, the storage log was filled with wheat for baking purposes. María Zapata, five-years old, played house on the white and brown *jerga* woven by Catalina's hands. Her father told her that this old pattern was used in the motherland of Spain.

Catalina kept the white box with her Toledo damascene brooch on the pine table. The two simple white and blue candleholders from Puebla decorated the table. Next to her children and her husband, this box protected her most prized possessions.

Peace cushioned the house in a protective invisible netting. Her neighbor, Juan Alonso Mondragón, owner of the *encomienda* of Senucú, used to tell her that he enjoyed visiting the Telles home because it was an oasis in the desert. He said that he would rather live in the country than in the city of Santa Fe because Santa Fe was deteriorating because building repairs and security measurements of the Palace were not being enforced. Catalina did not know if he was telling the truth because he was eighty-years old and she thought he was getting senile.

María Zapata was playing with a miniature brown ceramic pottery set her father bought her several years ago. As María was pretending to pour cold chocolate from a pitcher into a cup, Catalina saw something move near her daughter and let out a loud surprised gasp.

"María, do not move. Stay on the *jerga* and do not turn around," ordered Catalina as the frightened girl looked at her mother in bewilderment.

With Deborah strength raging through her veins, Catalina grabbed the willow stick in the corner close to her and quickly lifting the circular mass of coiled snake, she threw it against the wall and yelled for María to run out of the house to find her father.

Within seconds of what seemed like an entire morning, José was standing at the door. The dazed coiled diamond backed rattlesnake was only two feet away from Catalina.

"Be still, my love. Be very still," he whispered to his wife drenched in profuse sweat dripping down her white linen blouse.

He picked up the stick and wrapped the six-foot rattlesnake around the smooth willow stick and released the snake at the back of the house. The reptile slithered away across the bluff of the arroyo.

Now shaking with the realization of the danger in her own home, Catalina scooped her daughter up in her arms. She stroked Maria's braided hair and kissed her timeless eyes.

María gazed directly into her mother's emerald eyes and said, "Do not be afraid, my dear *Mamacita*. My angel was near me. The angel of our Law will always take care of me. Will you please make me some hot chocolate? I am hungry. Are there any more pine nuts for me to eat?"

For an instant, Catalina became Catalina López having breakfast at *Tía* Ana's home. She saw Luisa feasting on almonds and sweets.

Then from the depth of her ancient soul to the entryway of her heart, a presence of fear torpedoed through the peaceful veneer of her abode. A poisonous snake was in the center of her *casa*. What did this signify? She felt like Eve walking in the Garden of Senucú. This was a bad, bad omen. It was a time for building up strength for the future.

The province of New Mexico was racked restless and rebellious in August of 1680. Governor Antonio de Otermín, residing in Santa Fe, sensed a threatening energy approaching the fragile territory under the Spanish flag.

Unknown to Otermín, a San Juan medicine man by the name of Popé, escaped to Taos to plan a revolt. He was a clever shaman and organized a plan by including the participation of diverse marginalized Natives serving as slave labor for the Spanish priests and government. Telling the leaders of other pueblos and nations that the Indian gods were not happy with the dying Son and the mourning Mother, Popé urged his brothers and sisters to unite in the common goal of removing the foreigners from their lands.

He preached to them that by expelling the strangers, restoring Native agriculture and worshipping the Native gods would bring peace to the people once again. Only maize and beans, the crops of the ancestors, were to be planted. Popé promised that warriors would divorce their Christian wives and that for every Spaniard the warriors killed, a new wife of their choice would serve him.

Popé shared his knowledge that the *katsina* living in the *kivas* would return to the people when the Spaniards were driven away from the lands of the native people.

Like King Ferdinand and Queen Isabel, Popé issued the Popé Edict of Expulsion with his signature of the knotted cord ordering the expulsion of the Spanish colonists. On August 9, 1680, he sent two messengers with two cords constructed of maguey fiber indicating that the rebellion would occur in two days.

The first night of the new moon was chosen as the night of the uprising. Wise Popé knew that the triennial supply caravan with ammunition and horses from Mexico City would arrive about the fifteenth of September. On the designated day of no knots remaining on the cord, Indians were to destroy and kill all Spaniards.

On August 9th, Governor Otermín learned from the Tano Indians at San Marcos and La Cienega that an uprising was eminent. He tortured the messengers to decode the meaning of the knots.

The rebellion began on August 10. A century of slavery and desecration of Native beliefs ultimately erupted into Indian rage. All Spanish mules and horses were killed. The lack of the Spaniards having these animals would strengthen the Indian advantage because there were only 170 colonists able to bear arms on foot, while there were over 8,000 Indian fighters.

By sunset of August 10, a total of 401 settlers and 21 friars were killed in the rebellion. The colonists of Río Arriba, lands north of Santa Fe, sought shelter in Santa Fe. The settlers of Río Abajo, lands south of Santa Fe, gathered at Isleta.

In three days, all of Río Arriba, with the exception of Santa Fe, had been destroyed. For nine solid days, the City of Holy Faith was held captive by Pueblo and Apache Indians. One thousand colonists huddled together in the plaza. The ditch supplying water to the settlers was stopped by the Indians on August sixteenth. The same day, two thousand and five hundred

Indian soldiers destroyed the chapel. Fear and fright overtook the spirit of the colonists seeking protection on the plaza.

Water was finally restored to the plaza; however, the people had no food to eat. The putrid stench from dead animals and bodies stifled the air. Outside of the plaza, thousands of Indians, with others joining the group, waited for the final moment of battle.

There was no hope left. On August 21, Governor Otermín made one final attempt to leave Santa Fe. With firearms in hand, the colonists killed over 350 warriors as they fought their way to safety. The survivors formed a column with women and children in the center while the soldiers protected the whole group on the outside. Otermín was hoping to unite Río Arriba with Río Abajo at Isleta but learned from a messenger that Alonso García was leading this group to El Paso.

Walking on foot under the pounding summer sun, the colonists saw the Indians watching them and sending smoke signals to each other. In every village they entered, the expelled Spaniards found mutilated bodies and fires still burning. Marching through Cochiti, Santo Domingo, and San Felipe, more dead bodies were sighted. South of San Felipe, the naked bodies of Cristóbal Anaya and his wife, six children and four other household members were found in the *estancia* of Angostura.

Walking to stay alive, the colonists expected to see bloody sights in Isleta. Finally arriving at Isleta, they found nothing. Suspecting that the southern colonists were further south, Governor Otermín sent a scouting party ahead of the walking colonists.

On September 6, the Isleta and Santa Fe survivors united just near Socorro. Together, this group represented 1,446 colonists and 599 Pueblo and Apache Indians.

Governor Otermín settled the entire group in three camps around the Guadalupe mission. Of the near two thousand persons in the group, only one hundred and fifty one persons were capable of bearing arms. There were only four hundred and seventy one mules and horses. Nearly one thousand Spanish settlers lost their lives in the 1680 Pueblo Revolt.

Most of these colonists were descendants of the original 1598 settlers. Many of the pioneers left the Iberian Peninsula, sailed the Atlantic Ocean, traveled 2,000 miles by *carreta* from Mexico City to Santa Fe, served under austere governors and priests, were tried by the Inquisition and were now homeless in El Paso. Escaping with only their lives, and grateful for each breath they took, these destitute persons lost everything that they could not carry with them. In a strange way, they fled from their homes like they fled their Iberian homes per the Edict of the Spanish Expulsion and the Alhambra Decree.

During the next nine years, the drought was so relentless that the great Río Grande became a sand canal. It was a time to mourn for the Spanish Empire. It was a time to cry for the downtrodden souls of New Mexicans.

Catalina was tired beyond her chronological years. She endured the discrimination of Governor López tormenting her about her grandfather being a participant in the murder of Governor Rosas. She experienced her husband being jailed in Taos and their two *encomiendas* taken away from her family by Governor López. She lived through her cousins, Diego Romero and Francisco Gómez Robledo, being tried by the Inquisitors in Mexico City. She lived to see the terrors of the Indian Rebellion. Again, she was making a new home with her husband and children. She lost everything in her home, the *colchas*, silk shawl, dishes, *mantilla*, the gold and silver damascene brooch and every concrete memory of value. She lamented the loss of all of her personal items.

Like Job, she lost it all. But Catalina rejoiced in knowing that she did have her husband and her family. She was forty-two years old and felt like she was eighty-four. Since the Spanish settlers had been displaced by Indians in Santa Fe, they began to colonize El Paso del Norte. The pioneers suffered tremendous losses and most of them were fortunate to find the bare essentials of food and a roof over their heads to sustain them.

Time passed and in the winter of 1693 in Mexico City, the Countess of Galve heard the cathedral bells peal in joy over the re-conquest of the province of New Mexico by Diego Vargas. It was a time to rebuild the City of Holy Faith.

Now Catalina was fifty-five years old. Like Pedro Robledo, her grandfather, Catalina wanted to remain in El Paso and rest. She desired to walk along the riverbank and watch the birds fly above her head. She realized that she and José did not have much more time to live together. He was aging before her eyes and she was older too. Her hair was all white and her once smooth skin was now rough like worn leather.

Her children told her they wanted to remain with her in El Paso. María Zapata, her beloved daughter, wanted to return to her native home. María was attracted to Captain Diego Medina, a native of Durango. She wondered if the love she saw growing between these two young adults would be long lasting and prayed that the marriage between María and Diego would be strong. She prayed to *El Señor* that the guardian angel of María would watch over her daughter.

Doña María Zapata Telles Xirón married Captain Diego Medina, an officer, on January 26, 1694. Catalina Romero returned to the La Toma, near El Paso, for her final years. All of her children, with the exception of María Zapata, remained with her in the El Paso vicinity.

In 1695, Captain José Telles Xirón died. Catalina mourned the death of her life long companion. When he died, one eagle made his home in a cottonwood tree until José was buried. It was a time for dying; it was a season for mourning.

Endnotes

a   Poem by Isabelle Medina Sandoval

b   Hordes, Stanley M., *To the End of the Earth, a History of the Crypto-Jews of New Mexico*. New York: Columbia University Press, 2005, p. 62.

c   The little tiny black cat was seated upon his chair
with his finest stocking on and his fiber sandals too.
The information reached him that his marriage had been
arranged to a little dark-skinned kitten daughter of the
strutting cat.
So great was the cat's delight that he had a grievous fall;
his head was completely smashed and half of his back was broken.
"Bring someone, please, to confess him, the poor little cat in love."
"If I confess to you, my Confessor, that I have been a bad cat.
If I don't come out this, don't bury me in sacred ground;
Bury me in an *arroyo* where cattle may tramp upon me,
Let the *gachupines* say: "Here died the ill-fated one;
He did not die of sunstroke nor of a pain in his side,
He died from the pangs of love which he could no longer bear."
The mice on learning the news, in their great joy dress in red,
in the Spanish and French manner, in the style befitting soldiers.

Espinosa, Aurelio M., and J. Manuel Espinosa, ed. *The Folklore of Spain in the American Southwest*. Norman: University of Oklahoma Press, 1990, pp. 97-98.

d   I am crushing
little gold balls. Rap, rap.
Who is it?
I am the Bad Angel.
What does the Bad Angel want?

Colores.

What color?

Espinosa, Aurelio M. and J. Manuel Espinosa, ed. *The Folklore of Spain in the American Southwest.* Norman: University of Oklahoma Press, 1990, p. 171.

e   *Archivo General de la Nación, México, Tierras, t. 3268, pp. 234-250.* Albuquerque: Photocopies from Center for Southwest Research, Zimmerman Library, University of New Mexico.

f   Ibid., pp. 241-242.

Part IV
De Vargas New Mexico
1692 to 1810

1692

El Paso

La Reconquista

Chapter 19

Governor Diego de Vargas of New Mexico, in a letter to family members in Spain, described New Mexico--Spain's most northern frontier in North America--as an area so isolated that it could not be compared to another place. For almost one century, from 1598-1680, the Franciscan province concentrated on missionary efforts of the Pueblo Indians. Within this same eighty-year duration, the Holy Office of the Inquisition investigated issues of heresy, bigamy and Jewish practices of the colonists.

In New Mexico, wealthy citizens owned several hundred heads of sheep, cattle, oxen, horses, mules and irrigated open land. Imported linen, olive oil, clothing, dishes and religious articles were bought at premium prices for comfort in the frontier settlement. Citizens were accustomed to European and New Spain luxuries.

Before leading the *reconquista* of settlers in 1693, Governor Vargas experienced a full life. Born in 1643 in Madrid, he was raised in aristocracy and later found himself adapting to the complexities of bona fide life in New Spain.

In 1659, *Don* Alonso Vargas, father to *Don* Diego, died in Santiago, Guatemala. The Vargas family was respected for their military service. In 1083, three Vargas brothers assisted King Alfonso VI by protecting Madrid from the Moors. The Vargas family gave land to Francis of Assisi for a friary in Madrid and this family took pride in serving Spain.

Having lost his mother in childbirth during the birth of his sister when he was only five years of age, *Don* Diego was supervised by paternal relatives in Spain while his father lived outside the country. Meanwhile, *Don* Alonso, not having a college degree, made his fortune in Guatemala. He remarried and the day after making his will in 1659, while only in his late thirties, died. All of *Don* Alfonso's holdings in Spain were willed to his son Diego.

On April 1, 1664, *Don* Diego, a young adult of average stature and straight hair, married *Doña* Beatriz Pimental de Prado Vélez de Olazábel. Five children were born to his couple within six years.

Castile's economy from 1660-1670 suffered from inflation. Food staples such as wheat and cheese were too expensive for people to purchase. Potential droughts and floods plagued Castile. European cosmopolitan communities favored college educated persons.

With a large young family and having to settle his father's estate in Guatemala, *Don* Diego found his way to Santiago, Guatemala. When he arrived in New Spain, he realized that living in Spain without a college education would inhibit his voracious ambition. Having his father's genes, *Don* Diego saw New Spain as a fortuitous land of opportunity.

The 5,000 mile Atlantic voyage took two months to travel in 1673 and he went to Mexico. The contrast between Madrid and Mexico City was appealing to the determined young man. Many of the Spanish residents living in Mexico City had coaches trimmed in silk, silver and gold. The clean city was beautiful and refreshing in ambiance and diversity. The Mexican market was filled with native products as well as premium products from all over the world. A *gauchupin*, de Vargas adjusted to the harsh climate and the diversity of people. His homeland and Spanish upbringing influenced his dress and interactions with others. With his passion for clothing, he could not resist wearing a fancy cape with fine silver edging and a hat with a long feather plume. His personal dishes were made of sterling silver bearing his coat of arms.

His primary ambition was to make money to enhance his personal life style and social standing. Diego Vargas had petitioned the *Marqués* de Mancera for a position. He was sent by the government to work in the mining district of Teutila, two hundred miles away from Mexico City. While he was serving in his position as *alcalde mayor* in Oaxaca, he received news that his wife, *Doña* Beatriz, had died suddenly in 1674.

By 1690, *Don* Diego focused on the feasibility of enhancing his financial potential and attaining honor for reconquering New Mexico for the Spanish Empire. He had established and cultivated key political friendships in the New World, which would assist him in making his fortune. In truth, he desired to return to his natal land.

Dressed in a black hat with blue and white plumes, Diego de Vargas portrayed the image of nobility. His navy plush cape with metallic edging was certainly not the clothing of the ordinary man. His clothing was made with expensive linen lace and he carried an ornate gilded cane. He was a prominent man of means and his physical presence conveyed his social stature.

In El Paso, Diego de Vargas investigated the claim of a mercury mine in Hopi country. He spoke to Captain Juan Luis Luján, a *criollo* of eighty-six years of age, living in New Mexico since 1647. He also spoke to Captain José Telles Xirón, sixty years of age, living in New Mexico since 1647. These colonists shared their knowledge about the mercury mine.

In preparation for the expedition, Juan de Dios Lucero de Godoy, *Don* Pedro Ladrón de Guevara and Alfonoso Rael de Aguilar, advised *Don* Diego that each soldier for the reconquest would need a month's supply of biscuits, made from two bushels of flour and a two year old calf for jerky for food. In addition to these staples, and allotment of paper, tobacco and chocolate were to be provided to the soldier.

Governor Vargas wrote a letter to his son-in-law in Spain in spring of 1692 stating that he was prepared to provide munitions, arms, food and sharing of slaves to worthy citizens. His plan was in motion and he was committed to lead the expedition for Spain and G-d.

On Friday, November 21, 1692, the Mexico City cathedral bells pealed announcing that Governor Vargas would recover the province of New Mexico. A service of thanksgiving was held to pray for guidance and gratitude for this new opportunity to resettle the northern boundary.

In El Paso, on September 20, 1693, Sebastián Rodríguez, drummer and town-crier from the Angola nation for the de Vargas military, announced the approaching departure of Diego de Vargas to New Mexico. Energized settlers and onlookers were hopeful that the new expedition would yield positive results.

The beloved *La Conquistadora* would accompany the expedition along with Oñate's original royal standard. The wooden statue was brought to Santa Fe in 1625 by Fray Alonso Benavides, *comisario* of the Holy Office. *La Conquistadora* had been rescued from the fires of the 1680 Pueblo Rebellion in Santa Fe and was carried to El Paso.

On September 20, 1693, Diego de Vargas wrote a document that was made public in El Paso and in other surrounding areas. The official news to the citizens of New Spain was made in the plaza of the *pueblo* of El Paso that the settlers establishing homes in New Mexico would have the privileges and honors as established by King Carlos II.

José and Catalina Telles Xirón lived in Ysleta del Sur, now a section of El Paso. Escaping from their home in Senucú with only their lives, the couple, like the other fugitives, barely survived. De Vargas found the settlers in 1691 having few supplies to consume while surviving on mesquite fruit and *quelites* to stay alive. Accustomed to growing crops for food, the colonists found it difficult to find nutritious provisions in the desert. At least the colonists could draw fresh water from the Río Grande. Catalina invited José to take a walk with her along the Río Grande. The fall morning was cool and winter had already descended on the high peaks of the sandy, rugged mountains surrounding El Paso.

"José, who would have ever thought we would be living in El Paso? I really miss our home and the happy memories of our children playing at the *rancho*. As much as I would like to go back to New Mexico, I prefer staying here. I am just too old and tired to go back. What do you think? Maybe we should grow old together here? We certainly will not get fat eating wild spinach and mesquite fruit," joked Catalina.

José chuckled out loud and then roared with laughter, "My Catalina, I love your spirit. I can get fat on your courage and your determination."

The waking sun beamed on the golden cottonwood leaves barely moving with the gentle breeze. It was peaceful and quiet. Catalina took José's hand. "*Mi esposo*, I remember a family story of my grandmother walking with Pedro on the banks of the Río Grande. She said one of the best memories she had was walking with her husband along this river. Pedro admitted to her that he worked for the Office of the Inquisition to protect his family."

Nodding her head to the north, she added, "He died on that mountain on the *Camino Real* leading to Santa Fe. My grandmother planted his yellow roses of Castilla from the seeds he gave her from Spain. It was a promise she made to him that she would cultivate his flowers from Castile. Pedro finally admitted that he wanted to come to New Mexico to hide from the Inquisition."

Taking José's arm by her hand, she continued, "I have this poem in my heart. I know Grandmother's *rosas de castilla* have multiplied all along the *acequias* and towns in New Mexico. When I think of the beautiful yellow roses gracing the land, my heart is happy because I think of Grandfather. I remember how joyful our son, Rafael, appeared when he gave María Zapata the roses for her ceremony. The yellow roses are like the Jewish faith, they rooted and bear fruit. I wrote this poem to pay tribute to my grandfather and the flowers of our faith.

> *En el patio grande de mi ranchito*
> *Hay rosas nativas de mi abuelito*
> *Rama graciosa, ¿adónde vas?*
> *Puedes vivir aquí en paz.*
>
> *Fresca como el rocío de la mañanita*
> *Abre la flor tan bonita de la ramacita*
> *Con recuerdos de mi España querida*
> *Con corazón de mi España sentida.*
>
> *Linda como el sol de la tardecita*
> *Huele la fragancia suave de la rosita*
> *Preciosa es la linda rosa de Castilla*
> *Perfume dulce de riquezas de alegría.*
>
> *Fuerte como la luna de la nochecita*
> *Crece la rosa amarilla de la casita*
> *De raíces de tierra olvidada*
> *De vida de Ysrael encantada.*

En el patio grande de mi ranchito
Hay rosas nativas de mi abuelito
Rama graciosa de la Sefarad
*Puedes vivir aquí en paz.*ᵃ

José put his arm around Catalina's shoulder. "Do you know what I think? I know we need to live out our days near this peaceful Río Grande. We do need to plant some yellow roses though." Catalina laughed. High above their heads, a pair of eagle eyes peered through the dark amber cottonwood leaves. It was a time to rest.

Governor Vargas required an accounting of the former New Mexico settlers leaving El Paso for New Mexico. The January 1693 muster listed the following persons as heads of household. In total, there were 73 married couples, 115 widows, widowers and singles, 448 boys and girls and 250 dependents. The adult colonists included:

Captain Antonio Montoya, wife, María Hurtado
Captain Juan García Noriega, wife, Francisca Sánchez de Iñigo
Adjunct Antonio Lucero, wife, Antonia Varela de Perea
Regidor Diego Montoya, wife, Josefa de Hinojos
Captain José Tellez Girón, wife, *Doña* Catalina Romero
Sargeant Mayor Juan Lucero de Godoy, wife, *Doña* Isabel de Salazar
Sargeant Mayor Bartolomé Gómez Robledo, sister, *Doña* Ana Robledo
Captain Lázaro de Mizquía, wife, *Doña* María Lucero de Godoy
Adjunct General Diego Varela, wife, Mariana Fresqui
Captain Francisco Romero de Pedraza, wife, *Doña* Francisca Ramírez de Salazar
Captain Luis Martín, wife, Melchora de los Reyes

José Gallegos, wife, Catalina Hurtado
Andrés Hurtado, wife, Antonia Domínguez
Captain Juan Luis
Sargento Mayor Alonso García
Juan Perea, wife, Luisa de Tapia
Hernando Martín, wife, María Montaño
Cristóbal Martín, wife, Antonia Moraga
Juan de Rivera, wife, María García
Domingo de Herrera, wife, María Martín
Luis Martín, wife, María de Vega
Sebastián Martín, wife, María Luján
Pascual Cobos de la Parra, wife, Lucía del Castillo
Cristóbal de la Serna
Bartolomé Trujillo
Diego Durán, wife, Juana de la Vega
Agustín de Perea
Four Orphans in the household of José Tellez Girón
Catalina Esparza
Tiburcio de Ortega, wife, Margarita de Otón
Jacinto Sánchez de Iñigo, wife, Isabel Girón
Pedro Sánchez de Iñigo, wife, Lenor Baca
Mateo Trujillo, wife, María de Tapia
Augustín Luján
Juan de Archuleta, wife, Isabel González
Alonso García, wife, *Doña* Teresa Varela
Josefa de Fuente
Diego Romero
Ana María García
Josefa Durán
Juana de Herrera
Inés de la Cruz
Lenor Martín
Captain *Don* Fernando Durán y Cháves, wife, *Doña* Lucía
de Salazar

Pascual Naranjo, wife, María Romero
Manuel Gómez, wife, Antonia Ursula Durán
Lt. Governor Luis Granillo, wife, *Doña* Magdalena Varela
de Losada
Sargeant Francisco de Anaya Almazán, wife, *Doña* Felipa
Rico de Rojas
Sargeant Lorenzo de Madrid, wife, *Doña* Ana de Almazán
Captain Alonso del Río, wife, *Doña* María Gonzáles
Sargeant Cristóbal Tapia, wife, Juana de Valencia
Francisco Jurado, wife, Lucía Varela de Losada
Sargeant Sebastián González, wife, Josefa Rico de Rojas
Captain Juan del Río, wife, Ana de Moraga
Captain Pedro de Leyba, wife, María de Nava
Pedro Hidalgo, wife, Ana Martín Griego
Captain Pedro Madrid, wife, Guiomar Varela Jaramillo
Bartolomé Romero de Pedraza, wife, *Doña* Lucía Varela
Alonso Maese, wife, Catalina Montaño
Juan Pacheco, wife, Antonia de Arratia
Manuel Baca, wife, María de Salazar
Cristóbal Varela, wife, Casilda de Gracia
Antonio Cisneros
Augustín Luján, wife, María Cisneros
Sebastián González
Captain Francisco López, wife, María Moraga
Juan Varela, wife, Isabel Rico de Rojas
Luis Maese, wife, Josefa Montoya
Juan Griego
Juan Antonio, wife, María Magdalena
Captain Francisco Lucero de Godoy, wife, *Doña* Josefa
Sambrano
Doña Juana de Almazán
Doña Lucía Jaramillo
María Luján
Captain José de Padilla, wife, María López

Lázaro de Moraga, wife, Agustina de los Reyes
Captain Diego de Luna, wife, Elvira García
Francisco de Apodaca, wife, María López de Luna
Matías Luján, wife, Francisca Romero
Domingo Martín, wife, Josefa de Herrera
Francisco Romero, wife, Juana García
Pascual Trujillo, wife, Antonia Durán
Juan Trujillo
Agustín de Salazar, wife, Felipa de Gamboa
Antonio Durán
Inés Herrera
Francisca de Abrego
Diego Trujillo, wife, Catarina Griego
Ana de Abrego
Cristóbal Baca
Doña Ana Moreno de Lara
Ana María Montoya
Captain Juan de Valencia, wife, Juana Madrid
Alonso Rodríguez, wife, Juana Valencia
Cristóbal Trujillo, wife, María de Manzanares
Juana de Argüello
María Martín
Salvador Romero, wife, María López
Juana de Leyba
Juan de la Paz, wife, Pascuala de Archuleta
Tomás de la Cruz, wife, Ursula Gómez
Matías Francisco, wife, María Gómez
Juan de Archuleta, wife, María de la Cruz
María de Tapia[b]

On October 4, 1693, Governor Vargas ordered the expedition to leave El Paso with the colonists wanting to relocate or settle the *villa* of Santa Fe. Some former Santa Fe colonists decided to remain in El Paso. As this caravan of settlers and soldiers departed from the sandy mountains of the mesquite desert to the north, the collective anticipation of victory was shared by the colonists. For the settlers making La Toma their home since the 1680 uprising, the native crown of thorn cacti spines of sorrow, growing wild in the desert, pierced their heads and hearts. El Paso had been their home and this place of refuge was truly a paradise in the wilderness. These pioneers lived in poverty in El Paso because their worldly possessions were destroyed during the uprising. With each noisy turn of the wooden wheels of the *carretas*, emotions of joy, sadness and double thanksgiving creaked from the rotation of wagon wheels heading northward to resettle the province.

In the cold snow of December 16, 1693, this spirited caravan stopped at the walled *villa* de Santa Fe. People from nearby pueblos had been living in the city for more than a decade and refused to accept Spanish authority. By Christmas Eve, twenty-two infants were dead and buried in the cold ground. The colonists fought to regain their moment to live in this isolated settlement far from Spanish civilization.

On December 29, Governor Diego de Vargas ordered battle and after one day of intense fighting, reclaimed Santa Fe and the province of New Mexico for the Spanish crown.

For the descendants of the 1598 original settlers, like their mothers and fathers before them, they had survived. It was a season for hope. It was a time to rebuild.

Captain Cristóbal Velasco and Fray Francisco Farfán, a native of Cádiz, Spain, headed a separate 1693 settlement mission starting from Mexico City. In 1677, Velasco served as a convict in New Mexico and received no salary. He was a tall, freckled man with small eyes. This red bearded man married Josefa de Carbajal, daughter of María Márques. He fled from El Paso in 1682 and later distinguished himself as a captain for his service.

During the Pueblo Rebellion of 1680, Fray Francisco Farfán was a friar in Santa Fe and signed the decree on August 21 of that year to abandon the city. Fray Farfán was a defender of indigenous rights, and later in El Paso, he defended the case of the Manso Indians against Governor Domingo Jironza Petriz de Cruzate for the crime of garroting some of their tribal members.

On March 13, 1693, the Conde de Galve, Don Gaspar de Sandoval Cerda Silva y Mendoza, ordered a public proclamation be made in Mexico City to entice citizens to sign up to settle in the province of New Mexico. Genuine efforts were made to recruit settlers for the Velasco-Farfán settlement having the skills such as brick masons and stonecutters to assist in the recolonization labors of New Mexico.

Approximately 217 individuals made a nine-month journey from Mexico City to Santa Fe. On June 23, 1694, the Spanish colonists of the Velasco-Farfán Expedition arrived in Santa Fe to join the De Vargas settlers. Only Spanish colonists "legitimately married and of good character" were recruited.

Heads of the household of these families were:

- Miguel Gerónimo del Águila and wife, Gerónima Díaz Florido
- Antonio de Aguilera Ysassi and wife, Gertrudis Hernández Espinosa
- Gabriel de Ansures and wife, Felipa de Villavicencio Pérez Lechuga
- Ignacio de Aragón y Galindo and wife, Sebastiána Ortiz y Castro
- Jean L'Archiveque
- José de Atienza Alcalá y Escobar and wife, Gertrudis Sevillano Mancilla
- Juan de Atienza Sevillano

- José de Atienza Sevillano and wife, Estefanía Moreno de Trujillo
- Andrés de Betanzos
- Diego de Betanzos y Sosa and wife, María Luisa de Selorga
- Andrés Cárdenas and Juana de Ávalos Aldaña
- Francisco Lorenzo de Casados and wife, Ana Pacheco
- José de Castellanos and wife, Manuela de Paz Cortés y López
- Manuel de Cervantes and wife, Francisca Rodríguez
- Juan Cortés and wife, María Gómez de Ribera
- José Cortés del Castillo and wife, María de Carbajal
- *Don* Francisco Tomás de Espíndola y Espinosa and wife, *Doña* María de las Heras y de la Vara
- Juan Antonio de Esquibel and wife, María de San Nicolás Rangel
- Juan Fernández de Atienza Ladrón de Guevara and Teresa Fernández de Rivera
- José García Jurado and wife, Josefa de Herrera
- Miguel García de la Riva y Estrada and wife, Micaela Velasco Díaz
- Antonio de Godines y Estrada
- Petronila de la Cueva
- Francisco González de la Rosa and wife, Antonia de la Serna
- Jacques Grollet
- Tomás de Herrera Sandoval and wife, Pascuala de la Concepción Rivera
- Tomás Real de Hita and wife, Antonia Gutiérrez
- José Jaramillo Negrete y Palomares and wife, María de Sotomayor
- Tomás Jirón de Tejeda and wife, *Doña* Josefa González de Aragón
- Diego de los Reyes Jirón de Tejeda and wife, María de Leyva y Mendoza
- Nicolás Jirón de Tejeda and wife, Josefa Sedano Coronel
- Cristobál Marcelino Ladrón de Guevara y Orozco and wife, Juana de Góngora y de la Cueva

- Miguel Ladrón de Guevara and wife, Felipa Guerrero
- *Don* Francisco de Leiva
- Juan Luján Barba and wife, Petrona Ramírez
- Diego Márquez de Ayala and wife, María de Bolívar Palacios
- Juan Manuel Chirinos Martínez de Cervantes and wife, Catalina de los Ángeles Collacos
- José Bernardo Mascareñas Tobar y Quiñones and wife, María de Acosta
- Juan de Medina and wife, Juan Márquez Jaramillo y Zamora
- Juan Lorenzo de Medina and wife, Antonia Sedano Coronel
- Simón de Molina Mosquera and wife, Micaela de Medina
- Nicolás Moreno de Trujillo and wife, María Ruiz de Aguilar
- Antonio de Moya and wife, María Francisca Morales de Guijosa
- Pierre Munier
- José Núñez and wife, Gertrudis de Herrera Sandoval
- Nicolás Ortiz Ladrón de Guevara and wife, *Doña* Mariana Barba Coronado y Hernández de Salas
- Tomás Palomino and wife, Gertrudis Bautista Ulibarrí
- Juan de Paz Bustillos and wife, Manuela Antonia de Alanís
- Francisco de Porras and wife, Damiána González Gutiérrez
- Miguel Quintana Valdés Altamirano and wife, Gertrudis de la Santa Trinidad Moreno de Trujillo
- Antonio Rincón de Guemes and wife, María Fernández de Valenzuela y Castillo
- José Rodríguez and wife, María de Samano
- Juan Ruiz Cordero and wife, María Nicolasa Carrillo Terrazas

- Sebastián de Salas and wife, María García
- José Sánchez and wife, Josefa Gómez de Ribera
- Juan de Dios Sandoval Martínez y Estrada and wife, Juana Hernández
- Antonio Sayago y Segovia and wife, María de Mora
- Antonio de Silva and wife, Gregoria Ruiz
- José Ruiz de Váldez and wife, María Hernández Medina y Cabrera
- José del Valle y Enríquez and wife, Ana de Ribera
- Manuel Vallejo González and wife, María Gertrudis López de Arteaga
- Miguel José Laso de la Vega y Coca and wife, Manuela Hernández Medina y Cabrera José Velásquez Cortés and wife, Juana de Caras
- Francisca de Velasco

Another group of settlers, the Juan Páez Hurtado Expedition, from Zacatecas, arrived in Santa Fe on May 9, 1695. Juan Páez Hurtado recruited and headed this expedition of forty-six family groups. Unlike the rigorous screening of potential settlers of the Oñate and Velasco-Farfán parties, the Páez Hurtado Expedition of 1695 was organized in Zacatecas with questionable practices and motives. Charges of fraud were made against Juan Páez Hurtado. Some money to be paid to colonists on enlistment was not made as promised by Páez Hurtado. Vagabond Spaniards were recruited in gambling houses and efforts were made by the leaders of the expedition to recruit Black tamale makers in the Zacatecas plaza. Recruits consisted of Spaniards, *mestizos, mulatos* and Africans. After arriving in Santa Fe, colonists of this party complained of not having sufficient food to eat while en route to Santa Fe. The heads of households in the expedition were:

- Cristobál Aguilar and wife, Nicolasa Rinon
- Cristobál de Arellano
- José de Armijo and wife, Catalina Durán
- Nicolás Espinosa
- Bartolomé Lobato and wife, Lucía Ana Negrete
- Francisco Montes Vigil and wife, María Jiménez de Ancizo
- Juan Bautista Olivas and wife, Magdalena Juárez
- José de Quirós and wife, María de la Cruz
- Juan Felipe de Ribera
- Bernabé Rodarte
- Miguel Tenorio de Alba

Military men were important in enforcing safety and governmental standards of the citizens, church, government and the province. Surnames of these military persons serving from 1692-1696 were:

Alderete, Armenta, Ávila, Blea, Carrillo, Asillas, Contreras, Córdova, Fajardo, Fernández, Flores, Garduño, Giltoméy, Guerrero de la Mora, Hernández, López, Gallardo, Medina, Montes de Oca, Muñiz, Ojeda, Ortega, Páez Hurtado, Palomino Rendón, Peláez, Peña, Pineda, Rael de Aguilar, Ramírez, Rodríguez, Romero Cruz, Santisteban, Segura, Tafoya Altamirano, Ulibarrí, Rubalí, Valenzuela, Vargas, Vásquez de Lara, Villalpando.

Vargas was a literate man and possessed many books. In his personal library, he had three volumes of *The Mystical City of God*. Perhaps these texts assisted Vargas in gathering spiritual information relative to his exploratory endeavors. This religious work was written by Sister María de Jesús de Agreda, abbess of the convent of Franciscan Poor Clare nuns. Sister María was reported to have preached to Indians in Mexico and the Southwest without leaving her home in northern Spain. She was said to have appeared five hundred times to Indians by assisting them with conversion to the Catholic faith.

When de Vargas made his final will, he named Páez Hurtado as his attorney and executor of his estate. Don Diego de Vargas executed his will on April 7, 1704. He asked to be buried with military honors and the privileges of a titled nobleman of Castile. He specified that his personal silverware, bearing the coat of arms and jewelry consisting of diamond rings, pear-shaped pearl earrings and emeralds be sold. On April 8, 1704, Governor Diego de Vargas died apparently of dysentery, separated from his beloved family in Spain and alone in a land isolated from family.

It was a time in New Mexico when many people from diverse origins were almost ready to forge one community. Some surnames appeared suspicious, like Rael, shortened form of Israel. Nevertheless, it was a time for change and it was hard to monitor all the transformations taking place in a new Mexico.

1699

Guadalupe del Paso Blessing
Catalina López de Telles Xirón

Fifth Generation

Chapter 20

Catalina was exhausted. She had traveled over three hundred miles of desert from Santa Fe to the outpost of El Paso, returning to the land of the bones of her ancestors. The *villa* of Santa Fe was far away and had undergone many transformations since she had known it as a young girl. New families and soldiers were now pioneers making this place their home.

How could she return to her native city? Her maternal Archuleta grandfather was beheaded in the heart of the plaza and she was reminded cynically of this by Governor López de Mendizábal. Her husband was imprisoned in the Taos jail and she had to do without to provide for food for her children. Her two cousins were ordered to appear before the Holy Office of the Inquisition in Mexico City. All orders and decisions were formulated in the *villa* of Santa Fe.

La Toma, where Oñate held the first European Thanksgiving, was the place where the Robledo and López families had gathered originally with the other settlers and *conquistadores* on their journey to settle the unknown province over a century ago. This place of El Paso del Norte was a special place to her.

Resting near the Río Grande riverbank one afternoon, she saw many snow geese flying east. As she was meditating on the joys of her memories, she recalled telling her father that sometimes she felt as though she once lived in Toledo. Her daughter, María Zapata, told her that she knew she once lived in Egypt. This was a special gift of the women in her family.

Catalina felt a deep ache in her heart for María Zapata. Her daughter had fallen in love with a *soldado* and he had been sent to Santa Fe. Out of all her children, she felt closest to this daughter because they were so much alike. She would miss sharing their conversations and helping raise her future grandchildren.

As she looked to the east while drawing her last breath, the *Shekhinah* of the Eternal flapped near her face and she felt free to fly. Metallic golden wings underneath carried her upward. Flames of Friday night candles and the Torah powered her flight.

Sephardic grandmothers sang this song:

> *Mamacita mi hermana*
> *Tú eres mi hermana*
> *Que tus sueños*
> *Son mis sueños*
> *Semos hijas de Sara.*[c]

Situated nearby on Mount Robledo, an angel overlooked the landscape. Gabriel noted the New Mexico Promised Land correlated with the geography of Israel. All welcomed the *conversa* home. She was another survivor of the Spanish and Mexican Inquisitions in her family. It was a time for joy.

1776

Santa Cruz de la Cañada

María Paula Mascareñas de Sandoval

Ninth Generation

Chapter 21

A lively atmosphere of the strength of the *reconquista* of New Mexico was shared by the returning and new settlers. From Santa Fe, many families moved north from the *villa*. Santa Cruz de la Cañada, close to the original 1598 settlement of San Gabriel, was a favorite home of the settlers. As the families grew, husbands and wives settled in all directions to find sufficient land to support their agrarian life style.

The colonists had established a cohesive community. It did not matter to anyone if a family came on the first or the final expedition. Because of the small number of core colonists, men and women often married cousins. What mattered most was caring for each other and surviving. New relationships and new family members enriched the lives of the inhabitants.

María Paula Mascareñas exemplified this change. Not only was she related to Catalina López de Robledo through Catalina López de Telles Xirón, she was also related to Catalina López de Robledo by her grandfather, a Romero.

Holding her toddler daughter, slender five foot two María rocked Teresa de Jésus in her arms. When Teresa had closed her little eyes and fell asleep, María placed the two-year old girl on the mattress filled with soft lamb's wool.

Sitting down on the burgundy velvet chair belonging to her grandmother, Micaela Antonia López, María felt tired and needed a short nap. Placed on top of the small pine worktable, she kept the same paternal grandmother's tortoise shell box with thread, silver scissors and gold thimble to organize all her sewing items she needed for *colcha* embroidery.

In the corner of the room, on the adobe and black colored hound's-tooth *jerga*, was the loom that her maternal grandmother, Josefa de Medina, used to weave the woolen articles for her household and embroidery. María loved to feel the fine wool pass through her fingers. She heard the mothers of her mothers were weavers in Toledo, Spain.

María's son, Ubaldo, had a fat, brown and black striped cat, Calavera, that could be quite independent, but was presently curled up on the rug near the *fogón*. Calavera was a lazy cat and liked to sleep and have her stomach scratched. The cat followed María around the house when Ubaldo was not home.

Studying the church book belonging to her grandfather, Diego Antonio Romero, María heard the story that her great-grandmother, María López de Ocanto, kept written literature because she felt women should read. This love for deciphering books had been a secret dream María hoped to master. It was hard to find teachers in Santa Cruz. Instead of telling a story with wool and *sabanilla*, María wanted to translate the meaning to letters on paper with her thoughts and words.

The latest *colcha* she embroidered adorned the bed that she and her husband, Juan Antonio Sandoval, slept on each night. Bluebirds, embroidered with indigo dye she purchased from the caravan from Mexico City, decorated the cover. The background was oatmeal beige, the natural color of her *churro* sheep. In the corners, red pomegranates adorned the edges.

Yet there was this deep desire inside María to sculpt letters into thoughts rather than filling in yarn on the cloth. Hushed hours of conversations and teaching before she was born and grew inside her mother's womb, yearned to give birth to the script of her hand.

María sat down on the *jerga* carpet and petted Calavera. She purred loudly as María scratched her ears. Talking to the cat, her mistress said, "*Doña* Calavera, if I only had been born a male," María said, "I would read and yes, even write. There is an untold story that lives in my soul that must be told. I feel like I walked the streets of Toledo and walked along the Nile. Each time I feel like have another desert to walk and I keep looking for the meadowland where I can rest and watch my children grow strong. My soul is like a bird in flight and I seek to nest in my homeland, wherever it may be."

Calavera closed her eyes and rolled over on her back. With a lazy yawn, she stifled her response to seek María's attention by curling up next to her and going back to sleep.

Three years ago, knowing that a baby was growing inside her womb, María was on her way to church early one Sunday morning. As she looked to the bottom of the hill descending near the Santa Cruz Church, she saw two double rainbows arching over the church. She had never seen a rainbow in the winter and knew G-d was showing her a special sign. When she entered the church, she crossed herself and asked her Maker for understanding. María walked to her favorite church object, the Mexican painting of *Santa* Teresa. The artwork, a beautiful depiction of Saint Therese Ávila of Spain, represented the feminine aspect of feminine piety seeking spirituality. With the dove near *Santa* Teresa appearing to influence her writing, María was drawn to this painting because the bird reminded her of the eagles of the textiles she embroidered. María loved the painting so much that she named her unborn baby after the revered saint.

Her father had told her that *Santa* Teresa was her spiritual sister. Born in Old Castile, Saint Therese was the descendant of a *converso* grandfather, Juan de Toledo. This religious woman started the convent of the Carmelites and dedicated her work to poverty. *Santa* Teresa's special gift was deep prayer. Her father stated that it was really was a gift—this was the way Jewish women prayed. *Santa* Teresa prayed directly to her Maker, the same way Jewish women like Hannah prayed to Adonay. Juan Mascareñas reminded his daughter to pray directly to G-d for all her petitions. Her father stressed that *Santa* Teresa was known as a *conversa* mystic and believed in speaking to G-d without the intervention of others.

After her daughter Teresa was born, María sat for hours in the church communing with G-d while she sought advice from *Santa* Teresa. Alone in the church one Saturday morning, María was mediating on how to be a better mother because she did not believe in the Virgin Mary. As she was noting the detail of the dove interacting with *Santa* Teresa, she saw the figure of a priest examining the painting. Standing next to the priest was an older man. Looking into the face of the priest, she saw two fountains of tears that once were eyes. The old man behind the priest put his finger to his mouth and whispered to her, "Be careful when you baptize your children in secret and do not eat the first portion of your *masa*. Even when you think you are alone, the walls watch you. Don't fear the Inquisition, punishment, harm or disgrace. It is G-d, María, who encourages you with such important inspiration."

With the blink of her eyes, the two men vanished before her. María learned from others at church that the ghosts were sometimes seen inside the church. The priest was Father Juan de Tagle, former director of the Franciscan order in New Mexico serving from 1700-1725. The man who warned her was Miguel de Quintana, colonist of the Velasco-Farfán Expedition. Miguel was charged by Fray Manuel Sopeña in 1732 in Santa Cruz by the Holy Office of the Inquisition in Mexico City for heresy. *Viejitos* claimed Miguel read *Santa* Teresa's work and quoted her work frequently.

Realizing she needed to finish cleaning the house, María stood up to gather the broom and cleaning supplies. As she was dusting the wine colored velvet chair, her mother, Paula Romero, knocked on the door. Opening the heavy pine door to allow her mother to enter the thick walled adobe home, María hugged her as she walked through the doorway in a dignified manner. Fifty-seven years of age, Paula was an elegant woman. Her auburn hair, sprinkled with strands of gray, was pulled back into a severe bun at the nape of her neck. Wearing a medium weight black silk dress and black leather shoes, only a silver crucifix decorated the plain dress. Long silver Indian earrings matched the simple silver crucifix. Over her head and shoulders, a black silk *rebozo* with one foot long fringe on all sides, framed her cream white face. The oriental *rebozo* was embroidered with black roses and leaves.

Gently kissing María on the left cheek, Paula asked her daughter, "How are you, my daughter? How are you feeling? What are you doing?"

"*Ay, Mamacita*, I just put Teresa to bed now and was dusting the furniture. Today is Friday and I want the house to be clean," replied the daughter.

"My darling *hija preciosa*, you are so much like my grandmother, Catalina López. She was always dreaming and going on about her family. I used to get tired just hearing all of those old stories. Then I married Juan Mascareñas, *un portugués*, and now I see the impact on you. A Portuguese father and a *conversa* grandmother certainly altered your life. Why, pray tell, are you cleaning on Friday?" her mother asked.

"*Mamacita*, you know very well this is the beginning of *el sábado*. It is a holy day. Even the Catholic Church teaches that it is a sacred day. Come with me, let us walk to the back bedroom. Look, here on the table, I keep the two copper candleholders that Grandfather Mascareñas made with his own hands. I only light them on Friday nights and I hid them in the room with no windows."

Sighing heavily, Paula told her daughter, "The years have changed my daughter. Why light candles? Come to Mass with me on Sunday. We still worship the same God. Why do you light candles and do these crazy things? People will talk about you if they know. There is still an Inquisition and if you are caught lighting candles, you will be taken to Mexico City and thrown in jail. Your cousins were put in jail only one hundred years ago. Is this what you want? Do you want to leave your Teresita as an orphan?"

Toying with the gold *coqueta* filigree earring hanging on her small right ear lobe, María hesitated before she spoke. Smoothing her hair away from her temple, she said, "Let us go back to the front room. Please sit down on the velvet chair. I will make you some fresh chocolate. *Por favor,* sit down, my dear mother."

After preparing the hot chocolate with sugar, cinnamon and fresh milk, María mixed the beverage with the wooden eggbeater. She poured the chocolate from the copper pan into the blue and white Talavera mugs. "Here, *Mamacita.* This is just like the chocolate you used to make for me and now it is my turn to make it for you," she told her mother.

"I know that I trouble you with lighting candles on Friday," María told her mother as she handed her the hot mug.

She continued, "I know that your mother descends from the Romeros and Robledos. You descend from the *conquistadores* and their wives who came with Oñate. You are fortunate that your great-grandparents, Captain Diego Medina and Catalina Telles Xirón, survived the Rebellion. Even the shawl you wear is a reminder of your family because the Telles Xirón family remained in El Paso and sent you the gift of a silk shawl," she said putting down her own cooling half filled mug on the worktable next to her.

"Yes, my daughter. What you say is true. The Telles family is well known in the El Paso area. Years, plus miles, have distanced our kinship. My grandmother used to cry for her parents and tell me stories of the Inquisition. I am Catholic because I have a weak stomach and do not like any type of pain. In my heart, I will always be a believer in worshipping but only one God. However, we live in New Spain. Remember that Miguel de Quintana of Santa Cruz was taken before the Inquisition for heresy only thirty years ago. My daughter, I live in fear for you this very day. Please be careful," she pleaded with her daughter.

"Listen to me, *mi hija*," begged the mother. "Miguel was found innocent by the Inquisition because he exhibited "damage of the imagination" as demonstrated by his actions. In other words, they said he was crazy. He had been a respected notary and writer, but lost that. When Miguel died in 1748, he died from the pain of not having been able to express his literary talents for the rest of his life...I watch you my dear. Even when you are in church, I see you revering *Santa* Teresa more than our Blessed Mother Mary. I observe you looking at the saint and the dove guiding her written work. You, my daughter, have to realize that you live in Catholic New Mexico and this is your destiny."

Nervously moving away from Calavera as the cat stretched out her paw to scratch her expensive leather shoes, Paula added, "I remember my mother, Josefa Medina, telling me about Governor Félix Martínes' proclamation that the Edict of Faith was to be read to each person in 1716. After her parents came back to New Mexico from El Paso, she thought the Inquisition would wane. However, Fray Juan de Tagle was the *comisario*. The threat and the reality of Jewish heresy in New Mexico were very much alive."[d]

Mint green eyes penetrated her mother's soul as María responded, "I do hear you mother and I do understand. But please try to understand me. My father's family came with the *españoles mexicanos* of the Velasco-Farfán Expedition. We all know they were Portuguese Jews. Why, Gonzalo de Azevedo was born in Lisbon, Portugal. *Papá* told me that his great-grandfather was *Bachiller* Felipe Azevedo from Mexico City. He was educated and treasured books. His son, José Bernardo Mascareñas, was a coppersmith and he came to Santa Cruz because he wanted the freedom to worship away from the Inquisition in Mexico City," María told her mother.

After taking another sip of liquid from the mug, she continued, "Mother, they say that thousands of miles away from here, near the Atlantic Ocean in the New England vicinity, that the newly arrived English settlers are fighting a war for religious freedom against their mother country, England, and I sympathize with them. Here, in Santa Cruz, I want to worship the way I feel in my heart that is right for me to light Shabbat candles, to clean my house on Friday and to believe in one G-d. People say here that the Romeros were *conversos*. You are Romero too. Do you remember telling me the story of Cain and Abel and how Abel's blood cried out from the earth for justice over his death? Mother, your blood and my father's blood flowing through my veins cries out for spiritual justice this very day," emphasized María.

Paula was very quiet. Her left hand touched the outer edges of her silver crucifix. Then she sighed and in a resigned voice said, "María, they say that some women in our family have special powers. I can see that you are like your grandmothers. I am not inclined to be spiritual the way you are. Yes, I have heard about these English colonists too. In fact, I gave some old leather shoes and my old white silk shawl to help these poor people fight the oppression of the tyrannical English government. We old New Mexican colonists understand the hardships of these English settlers."

Nodding her head, she added, "I remember how my family told stories of our grandfathers thanking G-d at La Toma, a place near El Paso, in 1598. I think I understand you because this spirituality runs deep inside you. Hmm, you have your father's Portuguese blood and I have heard stories from him that they were escaping the Portuguese Inquisition. That is why the family came to Mexico City. The Mascareñas family reminds me of the Portuguese Gómez Robledo family. They are very united and strong-willed people."

"*Gracias* to the *Eterno* for understanding, Mother. I feel like I lived under the harsh rule of the Egyptian Pharaohs, listened to the rabbis of Toledo, studied Torah and Kabbalah. I saw where I sat in the cells when the Inquisitors imprisoned me in Spain. I just know. I wish I could read. I do want to be like *Santa* Teresa and would love to write and read like her. *Santa* Teresa said mental prayer was an open dialog with G-d. Father told me she was a *conversa* like me. Maybe my little Teresita will grow up to read and write. I want to read and study but there are few opportunities for this in the province of New Mexico," lamented María.

"You are extraordinary, my precious. I have not been a good role model for you and yet your Jewish soul desires the freedom to practice the belief of our people. You do frighten me at times," shared Paula.

"Do not be afraid, Mother. Where will I really learn to read at my age? But I can teach Teresa and I can counsel my children to seek G-d in their hearts," declared María.

"My daughter, you are the fruit of my womb. I see your eyes and they remind me of what my mother told me. She said that the spiritual women in our family had green eyes. Your eyes are the chile green of Santa Cruz with flecks of the sparkling copper of Lisbon," said her mother.

"Again, *gracias, Mamacita*. Maybe I will have to forfeit this dream of mine to learn how to read and write. The priests today still watch what we read. I have heard what they did to Miguel de Quintana and all he wanted to do was to write with freedom of expression. The Inquisition tried to kill his spirit. After two hundred years of living in the province of New Mexico, I would think that we could read any book we want to read. I even believe that my dreams belong to *El Eterno*," added María.

"My dear daughter," responded Paula, "I can only imagine what the future has in store for your children. I understand that José's mother was related to Miguel Quintana. I would wager that Miguel Quintana came from a *converso* family. If you are spiritual, can you imagine the questions your children will have?"

María laughed and said, "*Ay, Dio,* what a thought. Well, if my children can read and write, then I will be a happy mother!"

Paula and María hugged each other warmly. As the two women looked into each other's eyes, their souls prayed for religious freedom for the children and the children of their children.

Teresita's loud cry broke up the embrace. Paula went home to fix a big lunch while María tended to holding Teresita after waking up from her hour nap.

Santa Cruz, the settlement of the Spanish settlers established in 1695, was located approximately thirty miles north of Santa Fe. Nestled in the curvaceous sapphire rock formations of the high altitude mountains tinged with coral at sunset, the Spaniards called the mountains *Sangre de Cristo* because the snow on the mountains had a trace of red like the blood of Christ. The village, surrounded by ruby and amber sand mesas, was crowned by the cream pearl covered mountain tops. In the winter, the snow melted into streams descending into the lava canyons of the majestic Río Grande River. Settlers lived a Spanish pastoral and agrarian life. The first Spanish pioneers brought wheat, garden vegetables and seed for orchard trees with them. As descendants from Castile Spain, they brought the horses, cattle and sheep with them to preserve their traditions. The children of the settlers employed the same agrarian life style of their parents.

María and her husband, Juan Antonio, were in love with each other. Juan Antonio Sandoval was adopted by José Sandoval and Antonia Romero. This couple had two children, Teresita and Ubaldo.

182 Part IV De Vargas New Mexico 1692 to 1810

In 1783, María received sorrowful news that Juan Antonio had died when he was thrown from his horse, causing fatal internal injuries. Now María was a twenty-eight year old widow left with two children. She was burdened with the task of feeding and raising her daughter and son.

Almost as an answer to her prayers, Baltazar Trujillo asked María to marry him. He was five years older than María and had longingly admired her from a distance since she was a young girl. He was an honorable man and was respected for his stability. His ripe chokecherry eyes warmed his light olive complexion. María was in love again; it was a time for rebuilding.

1787

Chimayo

María Paula Mascareñas de Trujillo

Ninth Generation

Chapter 22

In the high forests of the *Sangre de Cristo*, the Trujillo family lived in a flat roofed adobe home near the *acequia madre*. A few miles from the home, the *Plaza de Cerro* was named as El Puesto de San Buenaventura de Chimayo by Fray Andrés García in 1768.

Originally, Chimayo was the location of a Tewa Indian pueblo that became a Spanish settlement with the re-conquest of 1692. Old Juan, an Indian, told María that his people call it *tsimayo* for "good flaking stone" in his language. At one time, the Spanish used the mica from this place to make windows for their homes.

The colonial plaza was an adobe square having only two entrances by alleys. The irrigation ditch ran through the plaza and provided water for the community. On the west side of the plaza, was the *oratorio* used for chapel services. Within the plaza, a tower provided the community with a physical defense for surveying potential danger to the inhabitants of the community. This adobe plaza was reminiscent of the architecture of medieval La Mancha. The tower strongly resembled the proud towers found in Spanish castles of Castile. Chimayo was the center of castles, crosses, eagles and roses.

Because Chimayo was located in the dense pine forest, the village was not like the warm climate of Santa Fe or Santa Cruz. Heavy snow blanketed the ground during winter months and travel was difficult because treacherous dirt roads were hard to climb. On ascending to Chimayo from the road, wagons had to move quickly up the mountain because off the ledge was a two hundred foot drop culminating in green pine trees becoming a needled prickly carpet of danger.

María Paula was making a warm dinner for Baltazar and the children. Her husband had been busy all morning watering the cornfield and wheat. Baltazar was a good man and treated his stepson, Ubaldo, like his own son. Ubaldo was ten and helped Baltazar water and cut the weeds in the garden.

From the window of the kitchen, María saw her men tending the garden. Ubaldo had medium olive brown skin just like his father. Baltazar was five feet and ten inches tall with a medium build with dark black hair and a heavy moustache. Baltazar had a trim and muscular physique that was pleasing to her eye.

The June day had a sweet smell of early summer. The May apple blossoms were gone and were replaced by lush green leaves with grape size maturing apples. The earth was pregnant with life. A strong kick inside her stomach made her wince. Will this be a boy or girl? María and Baltazar had a daughter last year and now she was expecting again. She only wanted the baby to be born healthy. The baby kicked again and this time María had to sit down. She chuckled and believed that only boys kicked this hard. She surmised that there would be a Trujillo son to join his father and Ubaldo working in the garden.

Stirring the copper pan filled with lamb's quarters and adding a good measure of spicy Chimayo chile, she put more water in the *olla* to reduce the risk of the wild spinach being burned. It took an entire afternoon of picking choice *quelites* to make one small pan of vegetables.

Next, she rolled out the wheat *tortillas* on the kitchen table and placed the first one on the griddle to cook. Turning it over to cook on the other side, she went back to work to roll out the next dough circle to replace the *tortilla* on the griddle. She measured the doneness of the *tortilla* because the cooked side turned into various pecan colored circles. Taking off the cooked *tortilla*, she placed it on the clean cotton dishtowel to cool on the table. Then she repeated the same process until a dozen fat *tortillas* were cooked. She stacked the *tortillas* and took the first *tortilla* she made and threw it out because the first *tortilla* was never eaten. She did not know why she threw the *tortilla* away. Her mother told her that the first *tortilla* was never to be eaten. María Paula followed the traditions of her mother and did not ask questions.

María remembered what Miguel de Quintana whispered to her at church. She was careful not to let others see her not eat the first *tortilla* she cooked. She observed other women eat the first bread but always followed her mother's guidance. Since the Catholic priests depended on the money from the colonists to pay for church expenses, they seemed to be oblivious at times to minor sins because of the money.

María stirred the pot of beans mixed with dry corn. Slowly adding dried green chile and onion to the liquid, a tasty hot soup would soon be ready for her men. Her family enjoyed eating soups and stews.

She had an hour to herself before the men would return to eat. Using her time wisely, María went to the wooden loom to start the *sabanilla* she was going to weave for the altar cloth for the pine table Baltazar had crafted during the past winter. As she wove the threads together with the purr of the loom, she prayed out loud:

"As far as east is from the west
The west is east sun in my breast.[e]

When she finished chanting this prayer, the baby kicked again with an emphatic amen. María thought that out of all of her children she had carried in her womb, she knew this child was going to require special attention from her when it was born.

The following month, on July 2, María delivered a healthy baby girl. María Paula named her daughter with the most Christian name she could possibly choose, María Jésus. She was a delicate baby, but she was to develop a strong self-determining spirit.

The afternoon of July 3, the priest baptized the new Trujillo daughter. The priest in the Santa Cruz Church baptized the baby in the presence of the parents and the godparents, Damasio Trujillo and María Dionisa Borrego. The new mother claimed she was not feeling well and asked to host a *fiesta* later in the month. As was the custom, the *padrinos* handed over the newborn *criatura* to the mother saying:

> *"Reciba esta prenda amada*
> *Que de la iglesia santa salió*
> *Con los santos sacramentos*
> *Y el agua que recibió."*[f]

Feigning keen tiredness after the ceremony, María told everyone she was feeling ill and needed to go home to bed. The *madrina*, María Dionisa Borrego, expressed her satisfaction that the baptism had taken place because she had feared that the baby might be a heretic and was in danger of dying without being baptized. Dionisa's best friend, Beatriz Vigil, voiced her satisfaction that the baptism had taken place because she did not want María Jésus to be a *judía* for lack of the blessed baptism.

After José left the house to feed the cows and goats, María took her newborn daughter into her private bedroom. Baltazar was a good Catholic man and she did not want him to know how she was going to perpetuate the female custom of washing off the Catholic baptism and asking for a guardian angel for her daughter. She waited to get out of bed until she heard Baltazar leave the house.

María Paula's mother, Paula Romero died several years ago. Had Paula been alive, the grandmother would have assisted her to wash off the Catholic baptismal fluids. In her *conversa* family, this was the custom of the women. She would perform this holy ceremony by herself and G-d would witness the faith of her heart and soul. G-d had answered Hannah's prayer and she knew that this blessing of generation to generation must be honored by her actions.

María poured water into a basin to remove all traces of the baptismal liquids from her baby's head. Gently placing her daughter in the lukewarm water, she scrubbed the baby so much that her pale brown skin turned blotchy red. She washed the baby all over and placed some seed pearls, turquoise and coral nuggets in the basin filled with the clean mountain water. She followed this same procedure with all her children. Drying the baby with a thick towel, she took the baby out to the mountain behind the house and lifted her up to heavens. In the pure air of the high altitude surrounded by royal purple wild irises, her melodic voice halted the celestial melodies of the songbirds as she chanted:

> *"Eterno Altísimo*
> *Mis sueños son Tuyas*
> *Mi hija es Tuya*
> *Tus hadas protegen mi hija*
> *Alabado es El Eterno*
> *Siempre, siempre, amén."*[*]

By the end of the first week of the baby's life, her eyes changed from amber gold to a muted pine green flecked with copper lights. Her eyes tracked the movement of anything approaching her.

When María held her baby with the mystical eyes, she thought of the conversation she and her mother had regarding certain women in the family having special powers.

She remembered her mother telling her that the green eyes represented a physical trait revealing a light of spiritual character.

María Jésus was a lovely child. Her hazel eyes sparkled against her medium brown skin. Rarely having to be reminded or scolded for misbehaving, she was an intelligent and loving child. She spent time asking her mother and father philosophical and religious questions while demonstrating a bottomless thirst for knowledge. In her soul, María recognized how much her daughter mirrored herself. It warmed her to know that the Jewish faith burned like the blue flame of the Shabbat candle in the next generation of her blood.

From the dryness of the reality of worldly deserts of history bridging the pathway to the heart of the daughter of the *conversa*, some shards of light illuminated Santa Cruz. In the desert of New Mexico, there was light in the darkness on the most northern frontier of the province.

From the wilderness of New Mexico, the chime of time stopped to marvel that three centuries of the Spanish Inquisition had tolled the bell in remembrance of the *conversa* women from the Iberian Peninsula still providing Jewish support and spirituality for their children.

The years passed by almost too quickly. María Jésus turned seven in 1794. Strangers stopped to admire the presence of this young girl with the commanding olive green eyes. She portrayed an air of calmness and had an extraordinary intuitiveness in discerning what was appropriate in a situation.

Baltazar and María Paula decided to make a trip to Santa Fe to sell wheat and some *jerga* woven by María. They loaded the wagon and spent one night camping along the life giving Río Grande before reaching the capital city. The September plaza in Santa Fe was filled with traders from Chihuahua bartering and negotiating with the local people for their business.

While her parents were occupied with trading their items for iron, tools, olive oil, sugar, dyes, chocolate, spices and fine fabrics, María Jésus positioned herself next to a post of the *portal* on the plaza where a crowd congregated. A disheveled military officer and a rich Santa Fe man were quibbling over a price. Then María saw a beautiful Indian maiden about her age in the center of the crowd. The native girl was embarrassed by the attention focused on her. The rich man's voice became louder and then he took out some silver coins from his black velvet pants. As a bald fat man with yellow teeth accepted the money, the young girl, in compliance with societal norms, put her head down and followed the rich man.

The wealthy man yelled, "Get moving. You will have lots of work to do in the house and you get no days off. I own you now."

María, dressed in her homemade woolen dress, compared the simplicity of her clothing contrasted to the rich fabric of the prosperous man. She realized that expensive clothes did not cover the nakedness of the soul.

María's eyes caught the young maiden's tear filled eyes. A sympathetic optical bond of two young girls soothed the injustice of the moment. As María looked around the corner, she saw the mother of the girl crying. A profound sadness filled her heart as she realized that mother and daughter would never see each other again.

On the way home from the active plaza, María Jésus told her parents what she had witnessed on the plaza. Baltazar embraced his daughter and said that he did not like the way Indians were treated. He added that such behavior was truly criminal.

That evening, while camping by the riverbank of the great river, María Jésus meditated on the sadness of the Indian girl. She knew she would cry being separated from her own mother.

While falling asleep on the hard ground wrapped in woolen blankets, she dreamed of the fat man writing something down on paper and giving the rich man a folded written paper. Then she saw the priest writing her baptismal date. She saw the words on the paper listing her parents. She saw priests recording the baptisms of her mothers before her. She saw the priest sitting at an immense table with a big white ceramic urn decorated with a blue cross and officiating at a trial.

Then she woke up. Sweat drenched her body and her heart was pounding with fear. Suddenly, a soft flutter of air brushed against her face. She went back to sleep and dreamed of being in Sinai.

When she woke up the next morning, again, she felt a soft wind caress her mouth. It was almost as if an angel had touched her upper lip and left a fingerprint under her nose and sealed her mouth and heart.

She remembered the Indian girl and reflected on the sadness of the separation of the mother and daughter. In her thoughts it seemed as though it were yesterday when she learned about the Law. It was wrong to steal a daughter from her mother. It was wrong for anyone to steal anything. The Law teaches what is right and wrong. It was definitely a time to lose.

Chimayo

1800

María Paula Mascareñas de Trujillo

Ninth Generation

Chapter 23

As the November fiery opal sun cocooned into nocturnal rest, the lapis sky was illuminated by the filmy silver tarnished clouds. Transparent sheets of twenty-four carat gold light frosted the lush meadows and pine trees surrounding the Trujillo household. A small herd of elk could be seen in the distance drinking water from the ditch.

"Baltazar, *gracias, gracias* for everything," whispered María Paula as she patted his hand.

Returning her pat by slipping his fingers underneath her small hand, he said, "The years have been good to us, my love. I am over half way through my life and you have given me six children. When I married you sixteen years ago, you were a widow with two small children. I thought we would not have any children. Our four sons and two daughters would make any man complete. I have raised your children as my own and the Sandovals are the same as my Trujillo children," he told María as he affectionately squeezed her hand.

"After Juan Antonio died, I thought I would never love another man again. You would not take no for an answer when you persisted in wanting to marry me. The day you put this gold ring on my finger and gave me these gold filigree earrings, I have belonged to you. I do thank you and appreciate the way you have been a father to my first two children, as if they were your very own," she said.

With his thinning silver hair shining in the setting sun, he said, "I love you and I love the land of my fathers. I know the day I die that our children will carry through their veins the inheritance of our blood to their own children. You have been such a good mother and wife. Why, our Ana is only four years old. And Ubaldo is in love and ready to get married to his bride. All of our children have been treasured by me. You have been an exemplary mother. The wish of my heart is that our children are blessed in all they do."

"*Gracias, mi esposo.* Your words honor me and I appreciate the support you have given me," she replied.

"Just in case you did not know this, I have been aware of your secret religious ways. I have never said anything but my parents knew your father was a Portuguese Jew. After we were married, I made you the table to place the copper candlesticks José Bernardo Mascareñas made. You put a cross on the altar with the candlesticks you always light on Friday nights. I hear you say *gracias a Dio* and never *gracias a Dios.* It took me a while to discover that you worshipped one God and not a plural God. I am proud of you. Just promise me that you will give the candlesticks to our María Jésus. You know, she is very much like you."

"*Ay*, my Baltazar. Here I thought all these years that I had been discreet in not revealing the passion of my soul. Yes, María Jésus is a special child. G-d gave us a strong daughter to preserve our faith and keep our love," she murmured.

"New events are changing the way we live. This is no longer the province of New Mexico where the king tells us that we are his loyal vassals. A new era is on the horizon. The French try to infiltrate our lands and the English want our lands too. I hear that the Indians in Mexico are angry about working in the fields and having no food to eat," answered José.

Putting his calloused hand to his cheek, he continued, "Our María Jésus sees these inequities too. Here, the Indians are not treated well either. They are being pushed from all directions around us by the English and the French who covet their lands because of greed. All of these poor souls are leaving their homes and their cultures. Reports are being circulated that Indians are now attacking us. Strange, we have lived here since 1598 and now we are the foreigners. What will our own children see with their own eyes, my darling wife?" Baltazar asked.

The dry climate had creased María's skin with fine lines around her eyes and lips. Half of her long braided hair was now gray and the setting sun sparkled on her silver hair and long gold filigree earring dangling on her long thin neck.

"My wife, do you think that if I put some of the miraculous dirt on our hearts from the magic soil of the *Santuario* that this will protect our children from these future dangers?" José asked his spouse.

"No, my darling. Only our prayers and blessings for our children to G-d help. Night is falling; let us end another wonderful day in our lives and thank G-d for life," quietly stated the pensive wife.

"By the way, *mi esposa,* in my Trujillo family, my relatives say that we are *conversos* too. I am just too elderly to understand all of these mysteries. I only wish to be an honest man with a simple heart."

The following day, María Paula walked to the *Santuario* and prayed in the chapel for strong hearts, minds and faith for her children. She prayed that her children would never forget the faith of their Jewish mothers and fathers. With the silver cross of New Christianity weighing her down with four hundred years of oppression, she prayed that the *Dio* of the entire world would bless and keep the children of her womb. María Paula prayed that *Santa* Teresa would help her Teresita and granddaughters master the art of reading and writing.

As she stood up from pouring her heart out to the Lord, she heard a noise coming from the bushes. As she parted the branches of the *rosa de castilla* foliage, she was startled to observe two eyes staring back at her. The dark brown eagle looked at her directly and did not move. A peace fell over her heart and she knew that the eagle was a good sign. It was a time to soar on the wings of the eagle.

1810

Chimayo

Gabriel

Ninth Generation

Chapter 24

*I bore you on eagles' wings
And brought you to Me...*

Exodus 19:4

Pausing to rest from his heavenly duties, Gabriel observed the province of New Mexico from the top of the towering Jicarita Peak in the Sangre de Cristo Mountains. Since monitoring Juan de Oñate establish his government at San Gabriel, New Mexico became a special interest to him because it bore his name. There was one Catholic feast day on September 29, honoring Saint Michael, Saint Raphael and Saint Gabriel. There was no one feast day designated for Gabriel. Juan de Oñate must have experienced a *converso* memory awakening in naming *San Gabriel* as the first Spanish settlement in the Southwest by thanking *Adonay* from his Jewish soul.

The Spanish, Portuguese and Mexican Inquisitions were reality. Jews in Spain endured a hundred years of persecution before the 1492 Alhambra Decree was issued. Passage to the New World provided a viable means of escape. Many crypto-Jews left Spain and Portugal seeking freedom to worship in a far away place. Another hundred years later, the province of New

Mexico was regarded as one of the most secluded communities in the New World.

Only ten years ago, Governor Fernando Chacón took timber from this northern frontier to build the first bridge in El Paso. La Toma, the site of the first 1598 European Thanksgiving, became El Paso del Norte. King Charles IV assisted Governor Chacón in completing this arduous bridge project. Without the timber from the remote forests to engineer the architectural structure, El Paso may have remained a small pueblo. This geographical link fortified Spanish dominion against the foreign intrusion of the French and English.

Despite the trials of living in this beautiful and harsh environment, there was a sense that the geographic isolation insulated residents from the outside world. The Indians were mistreated. The frontier was fueled by the selfish intentions of some individuals devaluing citizens as human beings.

The Spanish motive for Christianizing all Spanish citizens was devastating. The discrimination spurred by the 1492 Catholic expulsion was now at the brink of extinction. The *Camino Real*, blazed by Juan de Oñate, progeny of former Rabbi Solomón Halevi, provided a pathway for crypto-Jews to survive in a place known as "the end of the earth". Indeed, there was a time for everything under the sun.

Gabriel smiled thinking about María Paula de Mascareñas. She was a virtuous woman following the teachings of her mothers. She did not understand the legality of Torah to know how to follow Jewish law; however, her heart was in the right place. Under duress, her family had been forced to convert to Catholicism.

Baptism was the act to convert a Sephardic Jew to Catholicism. The baptismal service was an irreversible practice. The fact that mothers throughout the years washed off the Catholic baptism oils and water from their children demonstrated their faithfulness to Judaism. While this act may not have been considered to be halakic according to Jewish law, it was a sincere maternal active effort to repudiate Catholicsm and affirm Judaism. These brave mothers defied the Catholic Church and could have been found guilty of being heretics by the Inquisition. María Paula de Mascareñas died in 1810, the year that Padre Hidalgo declared independence in Mexico. The Mexican Inquisition was still in force at her death.

How could vestiges of Judaism still exist in the desert of the wilderness? What would her children do? How did these women and families persevere under such duress? How did they survive these Inquisitions?

Would their children and the children of their children live under the threat of the Spanish Inquisition? María Paula lived in a period of trial and turmoil. Because she was a noble woman, true to her faith, she was carried away on the wings of the golden eagle. Like the dove of *Santa* Teresa, the *conversas* of Spain and Portugal persevered. Like the phoenix of Toledo, the crypto-Jews of New Mexico survived.

It was a time King Solomon described as many experiences under the David blue skies and the *sabra* cacti. There was a season and a time for everything under the sun. It was a time to celebrate the blessings of *Hashem*. María Paula Mascareñas, a daughter of La Mancha and Lisboa, was an Iberian lamplighter in a new world. She was a *conversa* and guardian of hidden traditions.

Endnotes

a   In the big patio of my ranch
There are native roses of my grandfather
Gracious branch where are you going?
You can live here in peace.

Fresh like the morning dew
The pretty flower opens from the branch
With thoughts of my beloved Spain
With the heart of my sentimental Spain.

Pretty like the afternoon sun
Smells the suave fragrance of the rose
The pretty Rose of Castile is precious
Sweet perfume of happy riches.

Strong like the moon of the light
The yellow rose of the house grows
With roots of my forgotten land
Of life in enchanted Israel.

In the big patio of my ranch
There are native roses of my grandfather
Gracious branch of the Sefarad
You can live here in friendship.

Poem by Isabelle Medina Sandoval

b   Sálaz Márquez, Rubén, *New Mexico, A Brief Multi-History.* Albuquerque: Cosmic House, 1999, surnames of colonists, pp. 75-92.

c   My dearest mother, my sister
         You are my sister
         Your dreams
         Are my dreams
         We are the daughters of Sara.

         Poem by Isabelle Medina Sandoval

d   Spanish Archives of New Mexico, Series II, New
Mexico State Records Center and Archives, Santa Fe, New
Mexico. *Bando* ordering publication of Edicts of Faith, May 23,
1716. No. 269a, microfilm, reel 5, frame 551.

e   Poem by Isabelle Medina Sandoval

f   Receive this loving jewel,
         Who from the blessed church comes
         With the Holy sacraments
         And holy water received.

g   Eternal Highest One
         My dreams are Yours
         My daughter is Yours
         Your fairies protect my daughter
         Praised is the Eternal One
         Forever, forever, amen.
         Poem by Isabelle Medina Sandoval

Glossary
Of Foreign Words Or Phrases

abuelita: Grandmother, Spanish
abuelito: Grandfather, Spanish
acequia: Canal or ditch, Arabic
acequia madre: Mother ditch, Arabic
adelantado: Military title held by *conquistadores*, Arabic
Adonday: Lord, Hebrew
alcalde: Mayor, Arabic
alhucema: Lavender, Arabic
alma: Soul, Spanish
alzada/o: Uppity, Mexican and New Mexican Spanish
amor: Love, Spanish
Ángel Bueno, Ángel Malo: Game played by children, Good Angel, Bad Angel, New Mexico Spanish folklore, Spanish
anís: Anise, Spanish
anusim: Iberian Jews forced to convert to Christianity, Hebrew
auto de fe: Public announcement of sentences imposed on persons tried by the Inquisition and the public execution of these sentences, Spanish
ay: Alas, Spanish
bachiller: Bachelor degree, Spanish
bando: Proclamation, Spanish
barukh: Blessed, Hebrew
bizcochito: Cookie or biscuit made with *anís*; also prepared by *conversos* and Sephardic Jews, Spanish
bosque: Forest, Spanish
bota: Small leather wine-bag, Spanish
bretaña: Fine linen, Spanish
buñuelo: Fried fritter served with honey linked to Arabic culture in Spain; also prepared by *conversos* and Sephardic Jews called a *bimuelo*, Spanish
caballero: Gentleman, Spanish
cabañuela: Prediction of weather starting January 1 based

on counting the first twelve days of weather, each day
representing a new month, and then counting backwards for
another twelve days; term referencing "hut" and this New
Mexico word probably referred to the fall "Festival of the Jews
of Toledo," Spanish

cada oveja con su pareja: Proverb; each sheep associates with
another sheep or with its own kind, Colonial New Mexican
Spanish

calabaza: Pumpkin, gourd, Arabic

calavera: Skull, Spanish

canal: Gutter, Spanish

carreta: Cart, Spanish

catedral: Cathedral, Spanish

churro: Iberian breed of sheep brought to New Mexico in
1598, Spanish

cofradía: Spanish Catholic guild formed for the purpose of
brotherhood of the faith, Spanish

colcha: Embroidered coverlet tapestry made of wool, Spanish

comadre: Godmother, Spanish

comal: Griddle for cooking, Náhuatl

comisario: Agent of Holy Office investigating crimes against
the faith, Spanish

compadre: Godfather, Spanish

conquistador: Conquerer, Spanish

converso: Spanish convert to Christianity by willingness or
by force while maintaining elements of Judaism in secrecy,
Spanish

convivencia: Living together, Spanish

coquetas: Gold earrings with fringe dangles, New Mexican
Colonial Spanish

corda seca: Tilework technique used to create multicolored
glazed tile using dry rope in the firing, Spanish

corral: Enclosure or pen for livestock, Spanish

criatura: New-born child, Spanish

criollo: Creole, one born in a colony of European parents,
Spanish

cristianos lindos: "Pure" beautiful Christians, Spanish
Cristo: Christ, Spanish
Dio: G-d, singular, term used by *conversos* in Americas and
Spain to affirm one G-d, Spanish
don: Spanish title used before male Christian names, Spanish
Don Gato: Burlesque ballad when a beast plays a hero, Iberian
sixteenth century, New Mexican Spanish folklore, Spanish
doña: Spanish title used before female Christian names,
Spanish
Edicto de Fe: Edict of Faith stemming from Edit of Grace
established in 1514, was read in churches to warn heretics
and all persons, with an opportunity to provide information,
including hearsay, to the *comisario* of the Inquisition, Spanish
El Camino Real: The Royal Road from Mexico City to Santa
Fe, Spanish
El Eterno: The Eternal One, Spanish
El Señor: G-d, Spanish
empanada: Little breads filled with fruit or meat; also
prepared by *conversos* and Sephardic Jews, Spanish
encomendero: Agent receiving commission, Spanish
encomienda: Royal grant given to an individual; the Indian
had to pay tribute to the owner provided that the owner
provided individual protection and provided that the Indians
received Catholic instruction, Spanish
entrada: Formal entry into a new land, Spanish
esposa: Wife, Spanish
esposo: Husband, Spanish
familiar: Lay person of the Inquisition, Spanish
fiesta: Feast, Spanish
fogón: Fireplace, Colonial New Mexican Spanish
garbanzo: Chickpea; also prepared by *conversos* and Sephardic
Jews, Spanish
gauchupin: European Spaniard living in Spanish colonies, Spanish
gracias: Thankful, Spanish
haba: Fava beans, prepared by *conversos* and Sephardic Jews;
Spanish

hadas: Fairies, celebration held for newly born females and
males in Spain, Portugal and New Mexico by *conversos;*
guardian angels or *hadas* were petitioned to protect the child;
Spanish
Hanuka: Jewish Festival of Lights, *buñuelos* were served in
New Mexico around Christmas while Sephardic Jews fry
bimuelos, Hebrew
Hashem: G-d, Hebrew
hesed: Loving-kindness, Hebrew
hidalgo: Noble man or *hijo de alguien*, Spanish
hierbabuena: Mint, Spanish
hija: Daughter, Spanish
hijo: Son, Spanish
horno: Oven, Spanish
jerga: Coarse woolen cloth used for floor coverings, Spanish
judería: Quarter of town where Jews live; Spanish
judía/o: Infant not yet baptized, Spanish
Kabbalah: Mystical tradition of Jews, Hebrew
kachina: Life bringer, Hopi
La Conquistadora: Virgin Mary saint brought to Santa Fe in
1625 by Fray Alonso Benavides; taken to El Paso in 1680 and
returned with Diego de Vargas in 1692, New Mexican Spanish
La Jornada del Muerto: The Journey of Death referring to the
ninety mile route on the *Camino Real,* Spanish
La Ley de Moisés: The Law of Moses, Spanish
La Mancha: Largest geographic plain in the Iberian Peninsula,
province of Spain, Spanish
Las Doce Palabras Retoreadas: The Twelve Reversed Words,
New Mexican folklore with European, Persian, Arabic and
Jewish influences; in Iberian tradition was viewed as a
superstitious prayer, Spanish
limpieza de sangre: Spanish Inquisition term referring to
purity of Christian blood for three generations on maternal
and paternal lines, Spanish

Los Moros y Cristianos: Traditional presentation on horseback of the Moors and Christians with the purpose of possessing the Holy Cross, a play used to teach Catholic religion, Spanish
madre: Mother, Spanish
mal de ojo: Evil eye, a spell cast on a person, Spanish
mamacita: Mother dearest, Spanish
manchego: Hard sheep's milk cheese from La Mancha, Spain, Spanish
mantilla: Lace shawl, Spanish
mantón: Cloak, Spanish
marqués: Marquis, title of nobility, Spanish (Surname usually written *Márques* in colonial New Mexico documents)
marrano: Referring to "hog" or "pig" or "dirty" or used to describe converted Jews to Christianity, Spanish (perhaps forced convert, *mumar-anus*, Hebrew)
más vieja que Sara: Older than Sara, Spanish
masa: Dough for making bread, Spanish
mazapán: Islamic confection of ground nuts served as a dessert often after Friday night meals in Toledo, Spain and colonial Mexico; referred to as marzipan, Italian
mercado: Market, Spanish
mesa: Flat surface on top of hills or mountains, Spanish
mestizo: Person of European and Indian heritage, Spanish
mil: Thousand, Spanish
Modah Ani: Jewish prayer giving morning thanks when waking in bed, Hebrew
mulato: Person of European and Black heritage, Spanish
neshama: Soul, Hebrew
nobleza: Nobility, Spanish
noria: Well, Arabic
Nueva España: New Spain, Spanish
olla: Round earthen pot, Spanish
oratorio: Private place for prayer, Spanish
padrina/o: Godmother/Godfather
papá: Father, Spanish
paraje: Camping place, Spanish

pase: Pass, Spanish
patio: Courtyard of a building or home, Spanish
picosa: Spicy, Mexican and New Mexican Spanish
piñon: Pine nut, Spanish
plaza: Square market area, Spanish
pobrecita: Poor little thing, Spanish
por favor: Please, Spanish
portal: Porch, Spanish
portugués: Portuguese, Spanish
preciosa/o: Precious, Spanish
prendorio: Engagement ceremony in New Mexico, Spanish
presidio: Armed people grouped together for defense,
Colonial New Mexican Spanish
pueblo: Town, Spanish
pueblo menudo: Little people or persons of little importance,
Spanish
puesto: Post, Spanish
quelites: Wild spinach, lamb's quarters, Mexican and New
Mexican Spanish
quemadero: Place where convicts were burned by the
Inquisition, Spanish
querido/a: Beloved, Spanish
rebozo: Silk embroidered shawl, New Mexican Colonial
Spanish
reconquista: Reconquest, Spanish
romance: Ballad, Spanish
rosa de castilla: Yellow Persian rose Spanish colonists brought
to New Mexico, Spanish
sábado: Saturday or Jewish Sabbath, Spanish
sabanilla: Woolen homespun, Territorial New Mexican
Spanish
sabra: Cactus pricklypear, imported from the Southwest to
Israel; tough on the outside while soft and sweet on the inside,
Hebrew

samarra: Garment worn by penitent convicts of the

Inquisition as they were burned at the stake, Spanish
sambenito – Garment worn by penitent convicts of the
Inquisition, Spanish
sangre – Blood, Spanish
Sangre de Cristo – Mountain range in New Mexico and
Colorado with snow-capped mountains having red blood color
at sunset and sunrise, Spanish
santa: Saint, Spanish
Santa Hermandad: Citizen police force established in the
12th century to stop crime; King Ferdinand and Queen Isabel
approved *La Santa Hermandad* to provide for national law
and order, Spanish
Santa María de la Blanca: Old synagogue of Toledo, Spain,
Spanish
santuario: Sanctuary, Spanish
Sefarad: Inhabitants of the Iberian Peninsula, Obadiah 20,
Hebrew
sefirot: System of Jewish symbolism depicting tree of the
Kaballah, Hebrew
Semana Santa: Holy Week, Catholic religious observance
from last week of Lent and the week before Easter, Spanish
semos: We are, old version of *somos*, Colonial New Mexican
Spanish
Shekinah: Jewish Kabbalistic feminine aspect of G-d, Hebrew
Shema: Jewish prayer affirming the monotheistic essence of
Judaism, Hebrew
sinagoga: Synagogue, Hebrew
soldado: Soldier, Spanish
soterrano: Underground structure for storing vegetables,
Colonial New Mexican Spanish
tamale: Cornmeal stuffed with meat or other vegetables
wrapped in a leaf, Náhuatl
tía: Aunt, Spanish
tío: Uncle, Spanish
Toldoth: Generations, Toledo, Hebrew
Torah: Five books of Moses, Hebrew

torta: Flat bread, Spanish

tortilla amarilla: Whole-wheat flat bread, New Mexican Spanish

torta blanquesa: White flat bread prepared by *conversas*, Spanish

tortilla: Small individual flat bread; Mexican and New Mexican Spanish

tsimayo: Obsidian flake, Tewa

turrón: Nougat made of almonds or nuts, Spanish

Una Niña en el Balcón: Novelesque sixteenth century ballad about a lovelorn maiden rejected by a shepherd, Spanish

vecino: Neighbor, Spanish

velorio: Wake, Spanish

viejita: Old lady, Spanish

viejito: Old man, Spanish

villa: Special New Mexico settlement designated as a capital or royal city, New Mexican Spanish

Yunque Yunque: Ancient Pueblo near Chama River and Río Grande where Oñate established San Gabriel in 1598; Natives often transliterated as *Ohke*, Tewa

Zocodover: Market place in Toledo, Spain, Arabic

Zohar: The Book of Splendor, Hebrew

Historical Characters

Adeva de Romero, María - Wife of Bartolomé Romero and mother of Captain Bartolomé Romero I, born in Corral del Almaguer, Spain in 1563. She is a probable descendant of the Benadeva family, Jews of Sevilla.

Aguilar, Nicolás de Aguilar - Native of Yurirapundaro, Michoacán, he escaped to New Mexico after committing a murder near Parral. He was accused by the Inquisition in 1660 of infringing on ecclesiastical jurisdiction. His trial in Mexico City resulted in banishment from New Mexico for ten years.

Aguilera, Teresa de Roche - Wife of Governor Bernardo López de Mendizábal, born in Alexandria, Italy. Teresa was imprisoned by the Inquisition in Mexico City. After her husband's death during confinement in 1664, Teresa's trial was suspended. Her personal possessions were embargoed and she died a poor woman.

Anaya Almazán, Cristóbal - Born about 1626 in Santa Fe and arrested in 1661 by the Holy Office for heretical remarks and imprisoned for four years. He was punished in Mexico City by participating in a public *auto de fe*. Cristóbal, his wife and six children were killed in 1680 at his *estancia* in Angostura.

Archuleta, Juan – Grandfather of Catalina Romero de Telles Xirón. He was the son of the Oñate soldier, Asencio de Arechuleta of Guipúzcoa, Spain. His mother was Ana Pérez de Bustillo. He was beheaded for the assassination of Governor Rosas in 1642.

Ávila, Santa Teresa de - Born in 1515 as Teresa Sánchez de Cepeda y Ahumada in Spain, was known as Teresa de Ávila. Her father was a *converso* merchant. She established the order of the Discalced Carmelites and was finally recognized for her establishment of mental prayer. After the Santa Cruz Church in New Mexico was constructed in 1733, a Mexican painting of Santa Teresa and a dove adorned the church wall.

Carbajal, Luis - Burned at the stake in Mexico City in 1596 by the Mexican Inquisition for being a crypto-Jew. He was the nephew of the governor of Nuevo León.

Cervantes, Miguel - Born in 1547 in Spain and regarded as one of the world's most distinguished writers. He wrote the classic novel *Don Quixote.*

Castaño de Sosa, Gaspar - Born in Portugal, he led settlers from Nuevo León against the directive of Luis Velasco II to New Mexico in 1590. He claimed he received permission from Governor Luis Carbajal of Nuevo León. For leading the illegal expedition as well as being suspect of being a Jewish apostate, he was exiled to the Philippines. He died on a ship in the South China Sea.

Farfán, Francisco - Native of Cádiz, Spain, was a leader of the 1693 recolonization. He survived the 1680 Pueblo Revolt and was a friar.

Ferdinand II, King of Aragon - Married to Queen Isabel of Castilla, united his kingdom of Aragon with his wife's lands of Castilla to form the Spanish nation. King Ferdinand's grandmother was believed to be of Jewish ancestry.

Ferrer, Vicente – Born in 1350 at Valencia, Spain, of probable Jewish ancestry. A Spanish Dominican preacher, he preached for the immediate conversion of Jews to Christianity. Thousands of persons listened to his oratorical eloquence.

Gabriel – Stands by the throne of G-d. As a messenger of G-d, the angel defends Israel against its accusers.

Gikatilla, Joseph – Born at Medinaceli, Old Castile in 1248 and died in 1305. He studied under cabalist Abraham Abulafía and was a Spanish cabalist and writer.

Gómez Robledo, Francisco - Born in 1628 in Santa Fe to his parents, Francisco Gómez of Coina, Portugal and to Ana Robledo, native of San Gabriel, daughter of Bartolomé Romero and Luisa Robledo. He was accused of Judaical tendencies and tried by the Inquisition. He was accused of being circumcised and was found innocent in Mexico City of being a Jew. He returned to New Mexico and did not return to Santa Fe in 1693.

Halevi, Solomón - Born in 1351 at Burgos, Spain, was the Chief Rabbi of Burgos and became a *converso* in 1391 while serving as Archbishop of Cartagena with the Christian name of Pablo de Santa María. Juan de Oñate, *conquistador* of New Mexico, was a descendant of Solomón Halevi.

Hurtado Páez, Juan - Born in 1668 near Sevilla, Spain, to Domingo Hurtado and Ana Josefa Rubio. He served in the military at Parral and was a friend of Diego Vargas for many years. He led the expedition of 1695 from Zacatecas to Santa Fe and was accused of fraud for taking allowances for persons not making the journey. He died in Santa Fe in May 1742.

Isabel I, Queen of Castile – Born in 1451, her marriage to King Ferdinand II of Aragon forged the establishment of the Catholic Monarchs. Queen Isabel and King Ferdinand issued the Alambra Decree in Santa Fe, Spain, in 1492, banishing Moors and Jews from Spain not willing to convert to Christianity.

López de Mendizábal, Bernardo - Born in 1620 in Chietla, New Spain, was a governor in New Mexico. He was escorted to Mexico City from Santo Domingo and arrested by the Inquisition. He died during imprisonment being accused of being a crypto-Jew in 1664.

López de Robledo, Catalina - Born approximately in 1548 and wife of Pedro Robledo of Carmena, Spain. Her family background is unknown. Many crypto-Jews changed their residency and names to hide from the Inquisition.

Maimonides – Born in 1135 at Córdova, Spain and died in Egypt in 1204. Esteemed as one of the greatest Torah scholars, he was a rabbi, physician and philosopher. He wrote the *Mishneh Torah* and *Guide for the Perplexed.*

Martínes, Félix – Served as a soldier with Diego Vargas and became interim governor of New Mexico on January 1, 1716. On May 23, 1716, he ordered a proclamation that the Edict of Faith be published and read by *comisario* Juan de Tagle.

Martínez, Ferrán - Served as Archdeacon of Écija, near Sevilla, Spain. He preached against the Jews and advocated extermination of Jews. As a result of his inflammatory speeches, a massacre of several thousand Jews took place in Sevilla in 1391.

Mascareñas, José Bernardo – Born in 1667 in Mexico City and baptized at the Cathedral of Mexico by his parents, *Bachiller* Felipe Mascareñas and *Doña* Isabel de Tobar. The Mascareñas family descended from Antonio Mascarenhas and Catalina Suares, inhabitants of Lisboa, Portugal. The descriptor Portuguese was equivocal to being Jewish.

Mascareñas, María Paula - Born in 1755, was the daughter of Juan Francisco Mascareñas and Paula Gregoria Romero. She was the mother of María de Jesús Trujillo.

Medina, Diego – Husband of María Zapata Telles Xirón. He was a military officer originating from Durango and born about 1670.

Medina, Josefa – Born in 1695, was the mother of Paula Gregoria Romero. Her parents were Captain Diego Medina and María Zapata Telles Xirón.

Moctezuma, Isabel – Married to Juan de Oñate and granddaughter of Hernán Cortés and Isabel Moctezuma. Her mother was the daughter of Aztec Emperor Moctezuma II.

Oñate de Salazar, Juan - Born in 1552 in Zacatecas, Mexico to Spanish-Basque colonists. His mother, Catalina de Salazar, was a descendant of Solomón Halevi. His wife was Isabel Tolosa Cortés de Moctezuma. He was the 1598 *conquistador* of New Mexico and the first governor.

Popé - Organized Pueblo peoples against Spanish oppression on August 10, 1680. This was the most successful resistance against foreign rulers in North America.

Quintana, Miguel – Born in Mexico City in 1673 and died in Santa Cruz in 1748. His wife was Gertrudis Moreno de Trujillo of Mexico City. His parents were José de Quintana and Nicolasa Valdés de Cervantes of Mexico City. The Inquisition investigated his writings in 1732 for not being aligned with Catholic doctrine. While attending church in Santa Cruz, he viewed the Mexican painting of Santa Teresa de Ávila receiving the Holy Spirit in the form of a dove as she was writing.

Robledo, Alejo – Brother of Pedro Robledo of Carmena, Spain. He was living in Carmena, Spain in 1574. He was married to Catalina Díaz and had three children. He wanted to travel with his brother, Pedro, to Mexico City.

Robledo, Alonso – Born in Cimapán, New Spain in 1577 to Pedro Robledo and Catalina López de Robledo.

Robledo, Ana – Born in Carmena, Spain to Pedro Robledo and Catalina López de Robledo. Ana died at a young age.

Robledo, Diego – Born in 1571 at Maqueda, Spain to Pedro Robledo and Catalina López de Robledo.

Robledo, Francisca – Daughter of Pedro Robledo and Catalina López de Robledo. She married Juan de Tapia and was listed as his wife in 1607.

Robledo, Francisco – Born in 1580 at Valladolid, New Spain to Pedro Robledo and Catalina López de Robledo. He survived the jump at the battle of Ácoma.

Robledo, Luis – Born in 1558 in Carmena, Spain and was the nephew of Pedro Robledo. He lived with uncle for twelve of his first sixteen years.

Robledo, Luisa – Born near Toledo Spain, she was the daughter of Pedro Robledo and Catalina López de Robledo. She married Bartolomé Romero and was listed as his wife in 1597.

Robledo, Pedro – Born in 1578 at Temazcaltepeque, New Spain to Pedro Robledo and Catalina López de Robledo. He was killed at the battle of Ácoma.

Robledo, Pedro – Born in 1537 in Carmena, Spain. He was a *familiar* of the Inquisition in Toledo and married Catalina López. It is probable that the Robledos originated from the old Jewish quarter of nearby Toledo. He was *Alférez* for Oñate troops and died in 1598.

Rodríguez, Sebastián - Born in 1652 in Angola. He married Juana de la Cruz and was a drummer for Diego de Vargas.

Romero de Telles Xirón, Catalina - Born about 1641, she was the daughter of Bartolomé Romero III and Josefa de Archuleta. She was the wife of José Telles Xirón.

Romero Medina, Paula – Born about 1727, was the mother of María Paula Mascareñas.

Romero, Bartolomé - Born in 1557 in Corral de Almaguer, Spain. His mother was María (Ben)Adeva and his wife was Luisa López Robledo. He was *Alférez* for the Oñate troops. His father was Bartolomé Romero of Corral de Almaguer, a probable new Christian.

Romero, Bartolomé II - Born at San Gabriel in 1602. He was the son of Bartolomé Romero and Luisa López Robledo.

Romero, Bartolomé III - Born in 1627 in Santa Fe. He was the son of Bartolomé II and was mayor of Santa Fe. His wife was Josefa de Archuleta.

Romero, Diego - Son of Flemish father, Gaspar Pérez, and mother, María Romero, daughter of Bartolomé Romero and Luisa Robledo. He was tried for heresy by the Inquisition in Mexico City in 1660. He participated in a public *auto de fe* and was banished from New Mexico.

Romero, Matías - Son of Bartolomé Romero and Luisa Robledo.

Romero, Paula - Daughter of María Josefa de Medina and Diego Romero.

Rosas, Luis – Served as governor of New Mexico in 1637. He was assassinated by Santa Fe men for his involvement regarding the seduction of the wife of Nicolás Ortiz, one of the eight men beheaded for the murder of Governor Rosas.

Salazar, Fray Cristóbal - Served as a Franciscan friar and was a cousin of Juan de Oñate. The site of Paraje de Fray Cristóbal, situated near Socorro, New Mexico, was named after the priest where he probably died.

Sandoval, Juan Antonio – Born in 1749 in Santa Cruz. He was the adopted son of José Sandoval and Antonia Romero. He was the first husband of María Paula Mascareñas.

Sandoval, Teresa de Jesús - Born in 1775 in Santa Cruz. She was the daughter of Juan Antonio Sandoval and María Paula Mascareñas.

Sandoval, Ubaldo – Born about 1776 in Santa Cruz. He was the son of Juan Antonio Sandoval and María Paula Mascareñas.

Solomón - Was the son of King David and Bathsheba. Recognized for his profound wisdom, he organized the construction of the magnificent Temple.

Sopeña, Fray Manuel - Was a priest in the Santa Cruz Church and accused Miguel Quintana in 1726 of writing material contrary to Catholic doctrine and reported him to the Inquisition.

Tagle, Fray Juan – Served as the director of the New Mexico Franciscan order and was a *comisario*. Miguel Quintana was close to Fray Tagle and claimed to have seen the ghost of the dead priest in the Santa Cruz Church.

Telles Xiron, José - Born in 1632 in Los Altos de San Jacinto in Coyoacán. He was the husband of Catalina Romero.

Telles Xirón de Medina, María Zapata - Born about 1674 to José Telles Xirón and Catalina Romero. She was married to Captain Diego Medina.

Trujillo, Baltazar – Born in 1750 and was the second husband of María Paula Mascareñas.

Trujillo, María Jesús Trujillo - Born in 1787 to María Paula Mascareñas and Baltazar Trujillo.

Vargas, Diego de– Born in Madrid, Spain in 1643. He led the expedition from Mexico City in 1692 to reconquer New Mexico after the Pueblo Uprising of 1680.

Author's Note

The historical characters of Catalina López, Catalina Romero and María Paula Mascareñas are my grandmothers. As a student in public schools, I did not find authentic New Mexico history and contributions listed in textbooks. Marcos Medina, my maternal great-grandfather, wrote a journal in 1894. I researched family information in the journal for over forty years, which included reviewing numerous archival documents written in medieval Spanish. Since written documentation about specific circumstances and information was not available in texts, I gleaned valuable research from interviews with family members.

This book is historical fiction because I do not know all the facts. I employed history as a framework to describe the lives of real New Mexico women. I construct a "her story" rather than a "his story" found in traditional books. It was apparent that the traditions of my grandmothers were passed down from generation to generation. I am indebted to my maternal ancestors for preserving customs of our rich crypto-Jewish heritage. I am indebted to my paternal ancestors for guarding our traditions.

Bibliography

Archivo General de la Nación, México City, Mexico.
Albuquerque: Photocopies from Center for Southwest
Research, Zimmerman Library, University of New Mexico.
Baer, Yitzhak, *A History of the Jews in Christian Spain*, 2 vols.
Philadelphia: The Jewish Publication Society of America, 1992.
Chávez, Angélico, *Origins of New Mexico Families: A
Genealogy of the Spanish Colonial Period.* Santa Fe: Museum
of New Mexico Press, 1992.
Cobos, Rubén, *A Dictionary of New Mexico and Southern
Colorado Spanish.* Santa Fe: Museum of New Mexico Press,
1983.
Curtin, L.S.M., and Michael Moore, ed. *Healing Herbs of the
Upper Río Grande.* Santa Fe: Western Edge Press, 1997.
Ellis, Florence Hawley, *San Gabriel del Yungue.* Santa Fe:
Sunstone Press, 1989.
Espinosa, Aurelio M. and J. Manuel Espinosa, ed. *The Folklore
of Spain in the American Southwest.* Norman: University of
Oklahoma Press, 1990.
 Esquibel, José Antonio and John B. Colligan, *The Spanish
Recolonization of New Mexico.* Albuquerque: Hispanic
Genealogical Research Center of New Mexico, 1999.
Gerber, Jane S., *A History of the Sephardic Experience.* New
York: The Free Press, 1992.
Gitlitz, David M. and Linda Kay Davidson, *A Drizzle of Honey.*
New York: St. Martin's Press, 1999.
Hordes, Stanley M., *To the End of the Earth, A History of the
Crypto-Jews of New Mexico.* New York: Columbia University
Press, 2005.
Jaramillo, Cleofas M., *Shadows of the Past.* Santa Fe: Ancient
City Press, 1972.
Kessel, John L., ed. *Remote Beyond Compare, Letters of don
Diego de Vargas to His Family from New Spain and New*

Mexico, 1675-1706. Albuquerque: University of New Mexico Press, 1989.

Kessel, John L., Rick Hendricks and Meredith Dodge, eds. *To the Royal Crown Restored, The Journals of don Diego de Vargas, New Mexico, 1692-1694.* Albuquerque: University of New Mexico Press, 1995.

Liebman, Seymour B., *The Jews in New Spain, Faith, Flame, and the Inquisition.* Coral Gables Florida: University of Miami Press, 1970.

Logghe, Joan and Miriam Sagan, eds. *Another Desert, Jewish Poetry in New Mexico.* Santa Fe: Sherman Asher Publishing, 1998.

Medina, Marcos, *Unpublished Journal of Medina Family,* La Agua Negra, Mora, 1894.

Melammed, Renée Levine, *Heretics or Daughters of Israel?* New York: Oxford University Press, 1999.

Pearce, T. M., *New Mexico Place Names, A Geographical Dictionary.* Albuquerque: University of New Mexico Press, 1977.

Sálaz Márquez, Rubén, *New Mexico, A Brief Multi-History.* Albuquerque, Cosmic House, 1999.

Simmons, Marc, *The Last Conquistador, Juan de Oñate and the Settling of the Far Southwest.* Norman: University of Oklahoma Press, 1991.

Spanish Archives of New Mexico, Series II, New Mexico State Records Center and Archives, Santa Fe, New Mexico.

Tellez, Carlos P., *Tellez History and Genealogy.* Albuquerque: 1991.

Published with support from

Institute for Tolerance Studies
is a 501 c 3 organization that does research, publications,
workshops, and conferences on social justice and conflict reso-
lution, addressing issues ranging from ethnicity to religion,
language, gender, and freedom of speech among others.

CPSIA information can be obtained
at www.ICGtesting.com
Printed in the USA
FSOW01n1332280816
24296FS